TEACHER'S GUIDE

Connected Mathematics 2™

Kaleidoscopes, Hubcaps, and Mirrors

Symmetry and Transformations

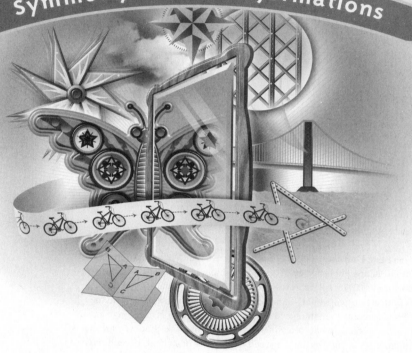

Glenda Lappan

James T. Fey

William M. Fitzgerald

Susan N. Friel

Elizabeth Difanis Phillips

PEARSON

Prentice
Hall

Boston, Massachusetts
Upper Saddle River, New Jersey

Connected Mathematics™ was developed at Michigan State University with financial support from the Michigan State University Office of the Provost, Computing and Technology, and the College of Natural Science.

This material is based upon work supported by the National Science Foundation under Grant No. MDR 9150217 and Grant No. ESI 9986372. Opinions expressed are those of the authors and not necessarily those of the Foundation.

The Michigan State University authors and administration have agreed that all MSU royalties arising from this publication will be devoted to purposes supported by the Department of Mathematics and the MSU Mathematics Enrichment Fund.

ISBN 0-13-165681-3

2 3 4 5 6 7 8 9 10   09 08 07 06

Authors of Connected Mathematics

(from left to right) Glenda Lappan, Betty Phillips, Susan Friel, Bill Fitzgerald, Jim Fey

Glenda Lappan is a University Distinguished Professor in the Department of Mathematics at Michigan State University. Her research and development interests are in the connected areas of students' learning of mathematics and mathematics teachers' professional growth and change related to the development and enactment of K–12 curriculum materials.

James T. Fey is a Professor of Curriculum and Instruction and Mathematics at the University of Maryland. His consistent professional interest has been development and research focused on curriculum materials that engage middle and high school students in problem-based collaborative investigations of mathematical ideas and their applications.

William M. Fitzgerald (*Deceased*) was a Professor in the Department of Mathematics at Michigan State University. His early research was on the use of concrete materials in supporting student learning and led to the development of teaching materials for laboratory environments. Later he helped develop a teaching model to support student experimentation with mathematics.

Susan N. Friel is a Professor of Mathematics Education in the School of Education at the University of North Carolina at Chapel Hill. Her research interests focus on statistics education for middle-grade students and, more broadly, on teachers' professional development and growth in teaching mathematics K–8.

Elizabeth Difanis Phillips is a Senior Academic Specialist in the Mathematics Department of Michigan State University. She is interested in teaching and learning mathematics for both teachers and students. These interests have led to curriculum and professional development projects at the middle school and high school levels, as well as projects related to the teaching and learning of algebra across the grades.

CMP2 Development Staff

Teacher Collaborator in Residence
Yvonne Grant
Michigan State University

Administrative Assistant
Judith Martus Miller
Michigan State University

Production and Field Site Manager
Lisa Keller
Michigan State University

Technical and Editorial Support
**Brin Keller, Peter Lappan, Jim Laser,
Michael Masterson, Stacey Miceli**

Assessment Team
June Bailey and **Debra Sobko** (Apollo Middle School, Rochester, New York), **George Bright** (University of North Carolina, Greensboro), **Gwen Ranzau Campbell** (Sunrise Park Middle School, White Bear Lake, Minnesota), **Holly DeRosia, Kathy Dole,** and **Teri Keusch** (Portland Middle School, Portland, Michigan), **Mary Beth Schmitt** (Traverse City East Junior High School, Traverse City, Michigan), **Genni Steele** (Central Middle School, White Bear Lake, Minnesota), **Jacqueline Stewart** (Okemos, Michigan), **Elizabeth Tye** (Magnolia Junior High School, Magnolia, Arkansas)

Development Assistants
At Lansing Community College *Undergraduate Assistant:* **James Brinegar**

At Michigan State University *Graduate Assistants:* **Dawn Berk, Emily Bouck, Bulent Buyukbozkirli, Kuo-Liang Chang, Christopher Danielson, Srinivasa Dharmavaram, Deb Johanning, Wesley Kretzschmar, Kelly Rivette, Sarah Sword, Tat Ming Sze, Marie Turini, Jeffrey Wanko;** *Undergraduate Assistants:* **Daniel Briggs, Jeffrey Chapin, Jade Corsé, Elisha Hardy, Alisha Harold, Elizabeth Keusch, Julia Letoutchaia, Karen Loeffler, Brian Oliver, Carl Oliver, Evonne Pedawi, Lauren Rebrovich**

At the University of Maryland *Graduate Assistants:* **Kim Harris Bethea, Kara Karch**

At the University of North Carolina (Chapel Hill) *Graduate Assistants:* **Mark Ellis, Trista Stearns;** *Undergraduate Assistant:* **Daniel Smith**

Advisory Board for CMP2

Thomas Banchoff
Professor of Mathematics
Brown University
Providence, Rhode Island

Anne Bartel
Mathematics Coordinator
Minneapolis Public Schools
Minneapolis, Minnesota

Hyman Bass
Professor of Mathematics
University of Michigan
Ann Arbor, Michigan

Joan Ferrini-Mundy
Associate Dean of the College of
Natural Science; Professor
Michigan State University
East Lansing, Michigan

James Hiebert
Professor
University of Delaware
Newark, Delaware

Susan Hudson Hull
Charles A. Dana Center
University of Texas
Austin, Texas

Michele Luke
Mathematics Curriculum
Coordinator
West Junior High
Minnetonka, Minnesota

Kay McClain
Assistant Professor of
Mathematics Education
Vanderbilt University
Nashville, Tennessee

Edward Silver
Professor; Chair of Educational
Studies
University of Michigan
Ann Arbor, Michigan

Judith Sowder
Professor Emerita
San Diego State University
San Diego, California

Lisa Usher
Mathematics Resource Teacher
California Academy of
Mathematics and Science
San Pedro, California

Field Test Sites for CMP2

During the development of the revised edition of *Connected Mathematics* (CMP2), more than 100 classroom teachers have field-tested materials at 49 school sites in 12 states and the District of Columbia. This classroom testing occurred over three academic years (2001 through 2004), allowing careful study of the effectiveness of each of the 24 units that comprise the program. A special thanks to the students and teachers at these pilot schools.

Arkansas

Magnolia Public Schools
Kittena Bell*, Judith Trowell*; *Central Elementary School:* Maxine Broom, Betty Eddy, Tiffany Fallin, Bonnie Flurry, Carolyn Monk, Elizabeth Tye; *Magnolia Junior High School:* Monique Bryan, Ginger Cook, David Graham, Shelby Lamkin

Colorado

Boulder Public Schools
Nevin Platt Middle School: Judith Koenig

St. Vrain Valley School District, Longmont
Westview Middle School: Colleen Beyer, Kitty Canupp, Ellie Decker*, Peggy McCarthy, Tanya deNobrega, Cindy Payne, Ericka Pilon, Andrew Roberts

District of Columbia

Capitol Hill Day School: Ann Lawrence

Georgia

University of Georgia, Athens
Brad Findell

Madison Public Schools
Morgan County Middle School: Renee Burgdorf, Lynn Harris, Nancy Kurtz, Carolyn Stewart

Maine

Falmouth Public Schools
Falmouth Middle School: Donna Erikson, Joyce Hebert, Paula Hodgkins, Rick Hogan, David Legere, Cynthia Martin, Barbara Stiles, Shawn Towle*

Michigan

Portland Public Schools
Portland Middle School: Mark Braun, Holly DeRosia, Kathy Dole*, Angie Foote, Teri Keusch, Tammi Wardwell

Traverse City Area Public Schools
Bertha Vos Elementary: Kristin Sak; *Central Grade School:* Michelle Clark; Jody Meyers; *Eastern Elementary:* Karrie Tufts; *Interlochen Elementary:* Mary McGee-Cullen; *Long Lake Elementary:* Julie Faulkner*, Charlie Maxbauer, Katherine Sleder; *Norris Elementary:* Hope Slanaker; *Oak Park Elementary:* Jessica Steed; *Traverse Heights Elementary:* Jennifer Wolfert; *Westwoods Elementary:* Nancy Conn; *Old Mission Peninsula School:* Deb Larimer; *Traverse City East Junior High:* Ivanka Berkshire, Ruthanne Kladder, Jan Palkowski, Jane Peterson, Mary Beth Schmitt; *Traverse City West Junior High:* Dan Fouch*, Ray Fouch

Sturgis Public Schools
Sturgis Middle School: Ellen Eisele

Minnesota

Burnsville School District 191
Hidden Valley Elementary: Stephanie Cin, Jane McDevitt

Hopkins School District 270
Alice Smith Elementary: Sandra Cowing, Kathleen Gustafson, Martha Mason, Scott Stillman; *Eisenhower Elementary:* Chad Bellig, Patrick Berger, Nancy Glades, Kye Johnson, Shane Wasserman, Victoria Wilson; *Gatewood Elementary:* Sarah Ham, Julie Kloos, Janine Pung, Larry Wade; *Glen Lake Elementary:* Jacqueline Cramer, Kathy Hering, Cecelia Morris, Robb Trenda; *Katherine Curren Elementary:* Diane Bancroft, Sue DeWit, John Wilson; *L. H. Tanglen Elementary:* Kevin Athmann, Lisa Becker, Mary LaBelle, Kathy Rezac, Roberta Severson; *Meadowbrook Elementary:* Jan Gauger, Hildy Shank, Jessica Zimmerman; *North Junior High:* Laurel Hahn, Kristin Lee, Jodi Markuson, Bruce Mestemacher, Laurel Miller, Bonnie Rinker, Jeannine Salzer, Sarah Shafer, Cam Stottler; *West Junior High:* Alicia Beebe, Kristie Earl, Nobu Fujii, Pam Georgetti, Susan Gilbert, Regina Nelson Johnson, Debra Lindstrom, Michele Luke*, Jon Sorensen

Minneapolis School District 1
Ann Sullivan K–8 School: Bronwyn Collins; Anne Bartel* (Curriculum and Instruction Office)

Wayzata School District 284
Central Middle School: Sarajane Myers, Dan Nielsen, Tanya Ravnholdt

White Bear Lake School District 624
Central Middle School: Amy Jorgenson, Michelle Reich, Brenda Sammon

New York

New York City Public Schools
IS 89: Yelena Aynbinder, Chi-Man Ng, Nina Rapaport, Joel Spengler, Phyllis Tam*, Brent Wyso; *Wagner Middle School:* Jason Appel, Intissar Fernandez, Yee Gee Get, Richard Goldstein, Irving Marcus, Sue Norton, Bernadita Owens, Jennifer Rehn*, Kevin Yuhas

* indicates a Field Test Site Coordinator

Ohio

Talawanda School District, Oxford
Talawanda Middle School: Teresa Abrams, Larry Brock, Heather Brosey, Julie Churchman, Monna Even, Karen Fitch, Bob George, Amanda Klee, Pat Meade, Sandy Montgomery, Barbara Sherman, Lauren Steidl

Miami University
Jeffrey Wanko*

Springfield Public Schools
Rockway School: Jim Mamer

Pennsylvania

Pittsburgh Public Schools
Kenneth Labuskes, Marianne O'Connor, Mary Lynn Raith*; *Arthur J. Rooney Middle School:* David Hairston, Stamatina Mousetis, Alfredo Zangaro; *Frick International Studies Academy:* Suzanne Berry, Janet Falkowski, Constance Finseth, Romika Hodge, Frank Machi; *Reizenstein Middle School:* Jeff Baldwin, James Brautigam, Lorena Burnett, Glen Cobbett, Michael Jordan, Margaret Lazur, Tamar McPherson, Melissa Munnell, Holly Neely, Ingrid Reed, Dennis Reft

Texas

Austin Independent School District
Bedichek Middle School: Lisa Brown, Jennifer Glasscock, Vicki Massey

El Paso Independent School District
Cordova Middle School: Armando Aguirre, Anneliesa Durkes, Sylvia Guzman, Pat Holguin*, William Holguin, Nancy Nava, Laura Orozco, Michelle Peña, Roberta Rosen, Patsy Smith, Jeremy Wolf

Plano Independent School District
Patt Henry, James Wohlgehagen*; *Frankford Middle School:* Mandy Baker, Cheryl Butsch, Amy Dudley, Betsy Eshelman, Janet Greene, Cort Haynes, Kathy Letchworth, Kay Marshall, Kelly McCants, Amy Reck, Judy Scott, Syndy Snyder, Lisa Wang; *Wilson Middle School:* Darcie Bane, Amanda Bedenko, Whitney Evans, Tonelli Hatley, Sarah (Becky) Higgs, Kelly Johnston, Rebecca McElligott, Kay Neuse, Cheri Slocum, Kelli Straight

Washington

Evergreen School District
Shahala Middle School: Nicole Abrahamsen, Terry Coon*, Carey Doyle, Sheryl Drechsler, George Gemma, Gina Helland, Amy Hilario, Darla Lidyard, Sean McCarthy, Tilly Meyer, Willow Nuewelt, Todd Parsons, Brian Pederson, Stan Posey, Shawn Scott, Craig Sjoberg, Lynette Sundstrom, Charles Switzer, Luke Youngblood

Wisconsin

Beaver Dam Unified School District
Beaver Dam Middle School: Jim Braemer, Jeanne Frick, Jessica Greatens, Barbara Link, Dennis McCormick, Karen Michels, Nancy Nichols*, Nancy Palm, Shelly Stelsel, Susan Wiggins

---

* indicates a Field Test Site Coordinator

Reviews of CMP to Guide Development of CMP2

Before writing for CMP2 began or field tests were conducted, the first edition of *Connected Mathematics* was submitted to the mathematics faculties of school districts from many parts of the country and to 80 individual reviewers for extensive comments.

School District Survey Reviews of CMP

Arizona
Madison School District #38 (Phoenix)

Arkansas
Cabot School District, Little Rock School District, Magnolia School District

California
Los Angeles Unified School District

Colorado
St. Vrain Valley School District (Longmont)

Florida
Leon County Schools (Tallahassee)

Illinois
School District #21 (Wheeling)

Indiana
Joseph L. Block Junior High (East Chicago)

Kentucky
Fayette County Public Schools (Lexington)

Maine
Selection of Schools

Massachusetts
Selection of Schools

Michigan
Sparta Area Schools

Minnesota
Hopkins School District

Texas
Austin Independent School District, The El Paso Collaborative for Academic Excellence, Plano Independent School District

Wisconsin
Platteville Middle School

Individual Reviewers of CMP

Arkansas
Deborah Cramer; Robby Frizzell (*Taylor*); Lowell Lynde (*University of Arkansas, Monticello*); Leigh Manzer (*Norfork*); Lynne Roberts (*Emerson High School, Emerson*); Tony Timms (*Cabot Public Schools*); Judith Trowell (*Arkansas Department of Higher Education*)

California
José Alcantar (*Gilroy*); Eugenie Belcher (*Gilroy*); Marian Pasternack (*Lowman M. S. T. Center, North Hollywood*); Susana Pezoa (*San Jose*); Todd Rabusin (*Hollister*); Margaret Siegfried (*Ocala Middle School, San Jose*); Polly Underwood (*Ocala Middle School, San Jose*)

Colorado
Janeane Golliher (*St. Vrain Valley School District, Longmont*); Judith Koenig (*Nevin Platt Middle School, Boulder*)

Florida
Paige Loggins (*Swift Creek Middle School, Tallahassee*)

Illinois
Jan Robinson (*School District #21, Wheeling*)

Indiana
Frances Jackson (*Joseph L. Block Junior High, East Chicago*)

Kentucky
Natalee Feese (*Fayette County Public Schools, Lexington*)

Maine
Betsy Berry (*Maine Math & Science Alliance, Augusta*)

Maryland
Joseph Gagnon (*University of Maryland, College Park*); Paula Maccini (*University of Maryland, College Park*)

Massachusetts
George Cobb (*Mt. Holyoke College, South Hadley*); Cliff Kanold (*University of Massachusetts, Amherst*)

Michigan
Mary Bouck (*Farwell Area Schools*); Carol Dorer (*Slauson Middle School, Ann Arbor*); Carrie Heaney (*Forsythe Middle School, Ann Arbor*); Ellen Hopkins (*Clague Middle School, Ann Arbor*); Teri Keusch (*Portland Middle School, Portland*); Valerie Mills (*Oakland Schools, Waterford*); Mary Beth Schmitt (*Traverse City East Junior High, Traverse City*); Jack Smith (*Michigan State University, East Lansing*); Rebecca Spencer (*Sparta Middle School, Sparta*); Ann Marie Nicoll Turner (*Tappan Middle School, Ann Arbor*); Scott Turner (*Scarlett Middle School, Ann Arbor*)

Minnesota
Margarita Alvarez (*Olson Middle School, Minneapolis*); Jane Amundson (*Nicollet Junior High, Burnsville*); Anne Bartel (*Minneapolis Public Schools*); Gwen Ranzau Campbell (*Sunrise Park Middle School, White Bear Lake*); Stephanie Cin (*Hidden Valley Elementary, Burnsville*); Joan Garfield (*University of Minnesota, Minneapolis*); Gretchen Hall (*Richfield Middle School, Richfield*); Jennifer Larson (*Olson Middle School, Minneapolis*); Michele Luke (*West Junior High, Minnetonka*); Jeni Meyer (*Richfield Junior High, Richfield*); Judy Pfingsten (*Inver Grove Heights Middle School, Inver Grove Heights*); Sarah Shafer (*North Junior High, Minnetonka*); Genni Steele (*Central Middle School, White Bear Lake*); Victoria Wilson (*Eisenhower Elementary, Hopkins*); Paul Zorn (*St. Olaf College, Northfield*)

New York
Debra Altenau-Bartolino (*Greenwich Village Middle School, New York*); Doug Clements (*University of Buffalo*); Francis Curcio (*New York University, New York*); Christine Dorosh (*Clinton School for Writers, Brooklyn*); Jennifer Rehn (*East Side Middle School, New York*); Phyllis Tam (*IS 89 Lab School, New York*);

Marie Turini (*Louis Armstrong Middle School, New York*); Lucy West (*Community School District 2, New York*); Monica Witt (*Simon Baruch Intermediate School 104, New York*)

Pennsylvania
Robert Aglietti (*Pittsburgh*); Sharon Mihalich (*Freeport*); Jennifer Plumb (*South Hills Middle School, Pittsburgh*); Mary Lynn Raith (*Pittsburgh Public Schools*)

Texas
Michelle Bittick (*Austin Independent School District*); Margaret Cregg (*Plano Independent School District*); Sheila Cunningham (*Klein Independent School District*); Judy Hill (*Austin Independent School District*); Patricia Holguin (*El Paso Independent School District*); Bonnie McNemar (*Arlington*); Kay Neuse (*Plano Independent School District*); Joyce Polanco (*Austin Independent School District*); Marge Ramirez (*University of Texas at El Paso*); Pat Rossman (*Baker Campus, Austin*); Cindy Schimek (*Houston*); Cynthia Schneider (*Charles A. Dana Center, University of Texas at Austin*); Uri Treisman (*Charles A. Dana Center, University of Texas at Austin*); Jacqueline Weilmuenster (*Grapevine-Colleyville Independent School District*); LuAnn Weynand (*San Antonio*); Carmen Whitman (*Austin Independent School District*); James Wohlgehagen (*Plano Independent School District*)

Washington
Ramesh Gangolli (*University of Washington, Seattle*)

Wisconsin
Susan Lamon (*Marquette University, Hales Corner*); Steve Reinhart (*retired, Chippewa Falls Middle School, Eau Claire*)

Kaleidoscopes, Hubcaps, and Mirrors
Symmetry and Transformations

Kaleidoscopes, Hubcaps, and Mirrors
Symmetry and Transformations

Goals of the Unit

- Understand important properties of symmetry
- Recognize and describe symmetries of figures
- Use tools to examine symmetries and transformations
- Make figures with specified symmetries
- Identify a basic design element that can be used with a transformation to replicate a given design
- Perform symmetry transformations of figures, including reflections, translations, and rotations
- Examine and describe the symmetries of a design made from a figure and its image(s) under a symmetry transformation
- Give precise mathematical directions for performing reflections, rotations, and translations in terms of the effect of the transformation on points of the original figure
- Draw conclusions about a figure in terms of the effect of the transformation on points of the original figure based on what symmetry or symmetries the figure has

- Understand that figures with the same shape and size are congruent
- Use symmetry transformations to explore whether two figures are congruent
- Give examples of minimum sets of measures of angles and sides that will guarantee that two triangles are congruent
- Use congruence of triangles to explore congruence of two quadrilaterals
- Use symmetry and congruence to deduce properties of figures
- Write coordinate rules for specifying the image of a point under particular transformations
- Appreciate the power of transformational geometry in the real world

Developing Students' Mathematical Habits

The overall goal of the *Connected Mathematics* (CMP) curriculum is to help students develop sound mathematical habits. Through their work in this and other geometry units, students learn important questions to ask themselves about any situation that involves the principles explored, such as:

- *How can I use symmetry to describe the shapes and properties of figures in a design or a problem?*

- *Which figures in a pattern are congruent?*
- *What parts of a figure will be matched by a congruence transformation?*

Overview

Students often have an intuitive understanding of symmetry. They recognize that a design is symmetric if some part of it is repeated in a regular pattern. Though students begin recognizing symmetric figures at an early age, the understanding needed to confirm symmetry and to construct figures with given symmetries requires greater sophistication. *Kaleidoscopes, Hubcaps, and Mirrors*, the last geometry and measurement unit in the Connected Mathematics 2 curriculum, helps students to refine their knowledge of symmetry and use it to make mathematical arguments.

Symmetry is commonly described in terms of transformations. Symmetry transformations, or rigid motions, include reflections, rotations, and translations. They produce congruent figures, as opposed to similar figures discussed in the grade 7 unit *Stretching and Shrinking*. Similarity transformations change the size of a figure while preserving its shape (unless the scale factor is 1 : 1). In contrast, symmetry transformations preserve both angle measures and side lengths, resulting in an image that is congruent to the original figure. The purpose of this unit is to stimulate and sharpen students' awareness of symmetry, congruence, their connections, and to begin to develop their understanding of the underlying mathematics.

Students will explore congruence, symmetry, and transformations in greater depth in future mathematics classes.

Summary of Investigations

Investigation 1

Three Types of Symmetry

Students are introduced to reflection, rotation, and translation symmetry. They identify the symmetries in several designs and make designs with given symmetries. Students are also introduced to tools and procedures for testing for symmetry and making symmetric figures. The goal is to heighten sensitivity to various forms of symmetry and to develop geometric techniques for testing and drawing symmetric figures.

Investigation 2

Symmetry Transformations

Students are challenged to describe the motions involved in constructing symmetric designs. They explore the relationships between figures and their images under reflections, rotations, and translations. They use their findings to write precise rules for finding images under each type of transformation.

Investigation 3

Exploring Congruence

This investigation emphasizes the connection between symmetry, transformations, and congruence. Students use their intuitions about what figures or parts of figures appear to be congruent. Then they use symmetry arguments to verify their intuition. The Side-Angle-Side, Angle-Side-Angle, and Side-Side-Side congruence conditions emerge from this investigation. Parts of the problem will reveal to students that congruence of quadrilaterals requires more information (in general 5 pieces of side and angle information suffice, but no less).

Investigation 4

Applying Congruence and Symmetry

Students are given some opportunities to reason with congruence conditions from Investigation 3 and symmetry arguments to establish congruence, and to use "corresponding parts of congruent triangles" to draw conclusions about side and angle measurements not available in the original data. Students also are asked to reason informally to conclusions about parallelograms and other figures. For example, if a quadrilateral has rotation symmetry, the quadrilateral must be a parallelogram, or the diagonals of a parallelogram bisect each other, and so on. This experience gives students an informal introduction to arguments like those they will use more extensively in high school geometry, without formal axiomatic reasoning.

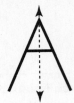

Investigation 5

Transforming Coordinates

Students work with figures drawn on a coordinate grid. By writing computer commands for making figures and their images under various transformations, students develop rules for locating the image of a general point (x, y) under a particular reflection, rotation, or translation, and use these rules to locate images under combinations of transformations.

Mathematics Background

In this unit, students study symmetry, symmetry transformations, and their connections to congruence. They learn to recognize and make designs with symmetry, and they learn to describe mathematically the transformations that lead to symmetric designs. They explore the concept and consequences of congruence of two figures by looking for symmetry transformations that will map one figure exactly onto the other.

Types of Symmetry

In the first investigation, students learn to recognize designs with symmetry and to identify lines of symmetry, centers and angles of rotation, and directions and distances of translations.

A design has reflection symmetry, also called mirror symmetry, if a reflection in a line maps the figure exactly onto itself. The letter A has reflection symmetry because a reflection in the vertical line through the vertex will match each point on the left half with a point on the right half and vice versa. The vertical line is the line of symmetry for this design. The image, or corresponding point, of each point on one side of the line of symmetry is the same distance from the line of symmetry as the original point.

A design has rotation symmetry if a rotation other than a full turn about a point maps the figure onto itself. The design below has rotation symmetry because a rotation of 120° or 240° about point P will match each point on each flag with a corresponding point on another flag. Point P is referred to as the center of rotation. The angle of rotation for this design is 120°, the smallest angle through which the design can be rotated to match with the original design. The image of each point is the same distance from the center P; and the original point, center P, and image point always form a 120° angle.

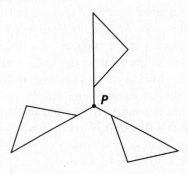

A design has translation symmetry if a translation, or slide, maps the figure onto itself. The figure below is part of a translation-symmetric design. If this design continued in both directions, a slide of 1 inch to the right or left would match each point of each flag in the design with a corresponding point on another flag. (Figure 1) Distances between corresponding points are all the same.

Figure 1

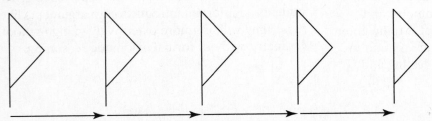

Making Symmetric Designs

Once students learn to recognize symmetry in given designs, they make their own symmetric designs. Students may use reflecting devices, tracing paper, and angle rulers or protractors to help them construct such designs.

- A design with reflection symmetry can be made by starting with a basic figure and then drawing the reflection of the figure in a line. The original and its reflection image make a design with reflection symmetry.

- A design with rotation symmetry can be made by starting with a basic figure and making $n - 1$ copies of the figure, where each copy is rotated $\frac{360}{n}$ degrees about a center point starting from the previous copy. The original and its $n - 1$ rotation images make a design that has rotation symmetry.

- A figure with translation symmetry can be made by making copies of a basic figure, so that each copy is the same distance and same direction from the previous copy. The figure and its translation images make a design with translation symmetry.

Students are being asked to develop two separate but related skills. The first is to recognize symmetries within a given design. The second is to make designs with one or more specified symmetries starting with an original figure (which may not, in itself, have any symmetries). Thus, it is important to give students experience both in analyzing existing designs to identify their symmetries, and also to give them experience using symmetry transformations to make designs that have symmetry.

Using Tools to Investigate Symmetries

There are a number of tools available that can help students visualize and describe symmetries. This section includes information about these tools and suggests some ways of using the tools.

Transparent Reflection

When using a mirror to test for reflection symmetry, it is hard to check the details of a design. It may be difficult to determine whether a reflected image matches the design behind the mirror exactly, since that part of the design is not visible.

Transparent reflection tools, such as Image Reflectors allow the viewer to see a reflected image while simultaneously looking at the rest of the object through the transparent plastic. This helps the user to match the reflected image with the part of the design behind the plastic. When the two halves match, the line of symmetry can be identified by drawing a line segment along the bottom edge of the plastic.

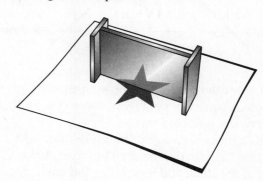

Hinged Mirrors

Using two mirrors, you can demonstrate the patterns made by reflections in a hinged mirror. You might allow students to experiment with the mirrors during this investigation.

1. Place the two mirrors at an angle facing each other. Tape the mirrors together so that they can be opened as if hinged.

2. Draw a dark line on a piece of paper.

3. Stand the mirrors on the line, positioned so that an equilateral triangle is formed by the reflections in the mirrors with the part of the line between the mirrors as one side of the triangle.

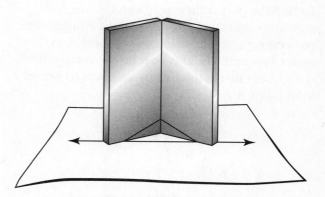

4. Reposition the mirrors by opening or closing the hinge to show a square, a pentagon, and so on.

5. Look for the lines of symmetry in each reflected image.

6. Place an object or draw a design between the line on the paper and the two faces of the mirrors; for example:

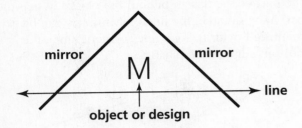

Now set the mirrors to show an equilateral triangle, a square, a pentagon, and so on, and observe the reflected images.

It is a nice extension to measure the angle between the mirrors for each polygon, make a table of the data, and generalize the angle needed to make an n-sided polygon by observing the pattern in the table. From the data below, it is evident that the angle of the mirrors necessary to produce an n-sided polygon is $\frac{360°}{n}$.

Angles Needed to Make n-Sized Polygons

Number of Sides	Angle of Mirrors
3	120°
4	90°
5	72°
6	60°

Finding Perpendicular Bisectors

To find the perpendicular bisector of the line segment connecting A to A' using a straightedge and compass, set the compass on point A to draw an arc that extends a bit beyond the midpoint of AA'. Using that setting, draw an intersecting arc from point A'.

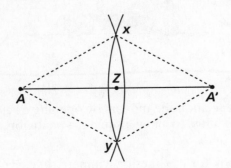

Draw the line connecting the points of intersection of the arcs. We can show that this line is the perpendicular bisector of $\overline{AA'}$. Note that the intersection points of the arcs, X and Y, are equidistant from A and A', that is, $\overline{AX} = \overline{A'X} = \overline{AY} = \overline{A'Y}$. We have a rhombus and its diagonals. From their explorations students know that the diagonal of a rhombus is an axis of symmetry; thus, $\overline{XY}$ is a line of symmetry. Because $\overline{XY}$ is a line of symmetry we know that the distance from A to the line of symmetry is the same as the distance from A' to the line of symmetry, and the line of symmetry is perpendicular to $\overline{AA'}$. Thus $\overline{XY}$ is also the perpendicular bisector of $\overline{AA'}$. (An alternative way of making a convincing argument would be to rely on showing there are four congruent triangles, which would allow us to deduce that $\overline{AZ} = \overline{A'Z}$ and $\angle AZX = \angle A'ZX$. Since these angles are supplementary adjacent angles they must be right angles.)

Students can find the midpoint of $\overline{AA'}$ using several informal methods:

- measuring to find the midpoint
- folding the line segment in half
- marking the length of the segment on a strip of paper and folding the strip of paper in half
- using a transparent reflection tool

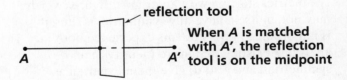

reflection tool

When A is matched with A', the reflection tool is on the midpoint

After locating the midpoint, students can use a square corner, an angle ruler, or a protractor to draw a perpendicular line through the midpoint. The idea of a perpendicular bisector is useful when students try to find an unknown center of rotation.

Symmetry Transformations

The concepts of symmetry are used as the starting point for the study of symmetry transformations, also called distance-preserving transformations or rigid motions. These transformations—reflections, rotations, and translations—relate points to image points so that the distance between any two original points is equal to the distance between their images. The informal language used to specify these transformations is *slides*, *flips*, and *turns*. Some children will have used this language and will have had informal experiences with these transformations in the elementary grades.

In this unit, students examine figures and their images under reflections, rotations, and translations by measuring key distances and angles. They use their findings to determine how they can specify a particular transformation so that another person could perform it exactly. Students learn that a reflection can be specified by giving the line of reflection. They learn that under a reflection in a line l the point A and its image point A' lie on a line that is perpendicular to the line of symmetry and are equidistant from the line of symmetry.

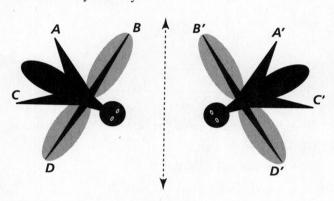

A rotation can be specified by giving the center of rotation and the angle of the turn. In this unit, the direction of the rotation is assumed to be counterclockwise unless a clockwise turn is specified. For example, a 72° rotation about a point P is a counterclockwise turn of 72° with P as the center of the rotation. Students learn that a point B and its image point B' are equidistant from the center of the rotation P. They see that the image of a point under a rotation *travels* on the arc of a circle and that the set of circles on which the image points of the figure *travel* are concentric circles with P as their center. They also find that the angles formed by the points on the original figure and their corresponding rotation

images, such as $\angle BPB'$, all have measures equal to the angle of turn.

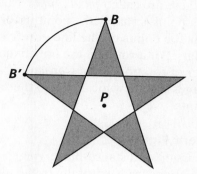

A translation can be specified by giving the length and direction of the slide. This can be done by drawing an arrow with the appropriate length and direction. Students find that if you draw the segments connecting points to their images, for example, CC', the segments will be parallel and all the same length. The length is equal to the magnitude of the translation.

This work helps students to realize that any transformation of a figure is essentially a transformation of the entire plane. For every point in a plane, a transformation locates an image point. And it is not uncommon to focus on the effect of a transformation on a particular figure. This unit attempts to give mathematically precise descriptions of transformations while accommodating students' natural instinct to visualize the figures moving. Thus, in many cases, students are asked to study a figure and its image without considering the effect of the transformation on other points. However, the *moved* figure is always referred to as the image of the original, and the vertices of the image are often labeled with primes or double primes to indicate that they are indeed different points.

An interesting question is, "For which transformations are there points that remain fixed?" These are called *fixed points*. The image of each such point is simply the point itself. For a reflection, the points on the line of reflection are fixed points. For a rotation the only fixed point is the center of rotation. For a translation, all points have images with new locations, so there are no fixed points.

Congruent Figures

The discussion of distance-preserving transformations leads naturally to the idea of congruence. Two figures are congruent if they have the same size and shape. Intuitively, this means that you could move one figure exactly on top of the other by a combination of symmetry transformations (rigid motions). In the language of transformations, two figures are congruent if there is a combination of distance-preserving transformations (symmetry transformations) that maps one figure onto the other. Several problems ask students to explore this fundamental relationship among geometric figures.

The question of *proving* whether two figures are congruent is explored informally from a different direction as well. A major question asked is what minimum set of equal measures of corresponding sides and/or angles will guarantee that two triangles are congruent. In the unit, students meet these ideas in an exploratory game situation where there is a payoff for finding the least set of measures needed to confirm congruence. It is likely that students will discover the angle congruence theorems that are usually taught and proved in high school geometry– Side-Side-Side, Side-Angle-Side, and Angle-Side-Angle. This engagement with the ideas in an informal way will help make the more proof oriented approach of high school geometry more understandable. They should also find that Angle-Angle-Angle and Side-Side-Angle do not guarantee congruence. Angle, angle, angle guarantees similarity, same shape, but not same size. With Side-Side-Angle, in some cases there are two possibilities, so you cannot know for certain that you have congruence.

In a right triangle, with the right angle and any two corresponding sides given you can use the Pythagorean Theorem to find the third side. This gives you two sides and the included angle, or

three sides—enough to know that two triangles are congruent.

Reasoning From Symmetry and Congruence

Symmetry and congruence give us ways of reasoning about figures that allow conclusions to be drawn about relationships of line segments and angles within the figures.

For example, suppose that line $\overline{AM}$ is a line of reflection symmetry for triangle ABC; the measure of $\angle CAM$ is 37°; the measure of $\overline{CB} = 6$; and the measure of $\overline{AM} = 4$.

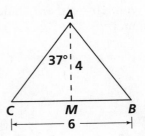

As a consequence of the line symmetry, you can say that

- C is the reflection of B.
- A is the reflection image of A.
- M is the reflection image of M.
- Segment CA is the reflection image of segment BA, which means they have equal lengths.
- Segment CM is the reflection image of BM, so each has measure 3.
- $\overline{AM}$ is the reflection image of $\overline{AM}$.
- So $\angle AMC \cong \angle AMB$; thus each angle meaures 90°.
- $\angle CAM \cong \angle BAM$, so each angle measures 37°.
- So $\angle C \cong \angle B$, and each angle must measure $180° - (90° + 37°) = 53°$.

In the grade 6 unit *Shapes and Designs*, students explored the angles made by a transversal cutting a pair of parallel lines. For some of the reasoning problems in this unit, students will probably need to use ideas of vertical angles, supplemental angles, and alternate interior angles from *Shapes and Designs*. For example, in the diagram below, *L*1 and *L*2 are given parallel lines and we know the measure of two angles. (We are not given that *L*3 and *L*4 are parallel.)

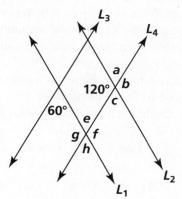

From this we can find the measures of angles *a, b, c, e, f, g,* and *h*. ∠*b* = 120° because vertical angles are equal. ∠*f* = 120° because alternate interior angles are equal. ∠*g* = ∠*f* = 120° because vertical angles are equal. ∠*a* is supplementary to 120° and, therefore, is 60°. This means that ∠*c*, ∠*e*, and ∠*h* are all 60° using vertical angles and alternate interior angles. We can then go on to say that *L*3 and *L*4 must be parallel because we know that alternate interior angles are congruent, ∠*e* and the angle marked as 60°.

The relationships among parallel lines and their respective transversals can help especially when reasoning about parallelograms. For example, in the parallelogram shown below we know, by definition, that there are two pairs of parallel lines and transversals. This relationship results in several pairs of congruent angles.

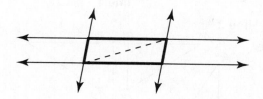

This prior reasoning from parallel lines cut by a transversal combined with congruence and symmetry culminate in *Shapes and Designs,* Investigation 4.3. Here students are asked to think about what is given in a quadrilateral and to draw conclusions about whether or not the shape is a parallelogram.

Coordinate Rules for Symmetry Transformations

In the final investigation of the unit, we look at transformations of figures on a coordinate plane.

Students also write rules for describing reflections of figures drawn on a coordinate grid. Such rules tell how to find the image of a general point (x, y) under a reflection. For example, a reflection in the *y*-axis matches (x, y) to $(-x, y)$; a reflection in the *x*-axis matches (x, y) to $(x, -y)$; and a reflection in the line $y = x$ matches (x, y) to (y, x).

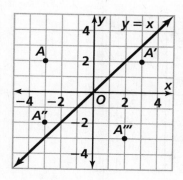

A' is the image of *A* under a reflection in the *y*-axis.
A'' is the image of *A* under a reflection in the *x*-axis.
A''' is the image of *A* under a reflection in the line $y = x$.

As with reflections, students learn to specify certain rotations by giving rules for locating the image of a general point (x, y). For example, a rotation of 90° about the origin matches the point (x, y) to the image point $(-y, x)$, and a rotation of 180° about the origin matches (x, y) to $(-x, -y)$.

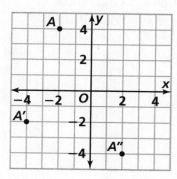

A' is the image of *A* under a 90° rotation about the origin.
A'' is the image of *A* under a 180° rotation about the origin.

A translation can also be specified by giving a rule for locating the image of a general point (x, y). For example, a vertical translation of 3 units up matches point (x, y) to $(x, y + 3)$, and a horizontal translation of 3 units to the right matches (x, y) to $(x + 3, y)$. A translation along an oblique line can be specified by considering the vertical and horizontal components of the slide. For example, a translation in the direction of the line $y = x$, two units right and two units up, matches (x, y) to $(x + 2, y + 2)$. A translation of 2 units to the right and 4 units down matches (x, y) to $(x + 2, y - 4)$.

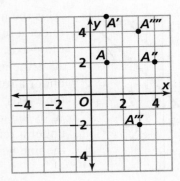

A' is the image of A under a translation of 3 units up.

A'' is the image of A under a translation of 3 units to the right.

A''' is the image of A under a translation of 2 units to the right and 4 units down.

A'''' is the image of A under a translation in the direction of the line $y = x$, 2 units right and 2 units up.

Combining Transformations

In very informal ways, students explore combinations of transformations. In a few instances in the ACE extensions, students are asked to try to describe a single transformation that will give the same result as a given combination. For example, reflecting a figure in a line and then reflecting the image in a parallel line has the same result as translating the figure in a direction perpendicular to the reflection lines for a distance equal to twice that between the lines.

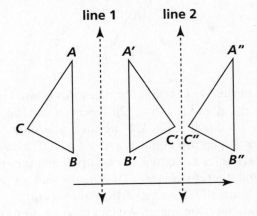

Reflecting a figure in a line and then reflecting the image in an intersecting line has the same result as rotating the original figure about the intersection point of the lines for an angle equal to twice that formed by the reflection lines. Notice that reflecting the triangle ABC in line 1 and then reflecting the image $A'B'C'$ in line 2 does NOT give the same result as reflecting triangle ABC in line 2 first and then reflecting the image in line 1.

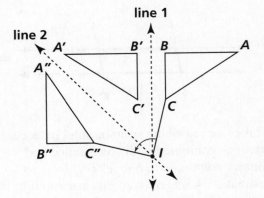

Students revisit this idea in the project when they explore combinations of transformations that map a geometric figure onto itself. In this instance, the figure used is an equilateral triangle.

Content Connections to Other Units

Big Idea	Prior Work	Future Work
Recognizing symmetry in designs Determining the design element that has been reflected, rotated, or translated to produce a design with symmetry Making designs with reflection, rotation, or translation symmetries	Recognizing and completing mirror reflections (*Shapes and Designs*) Recognizing and completing designs with rotation symmetry (*Shapes and Designs*) Rotating cube buildings (*Ruins of Montarek,* © 2004) Recognizing, analyzing, and producing tessellations (*Shapes and Designs*)	Recognizing symmetry in graphs of functions (high school) Applying the ideas of symmetry to other subjects, such as graphic design and architecture (high school)
Looking for patterns that can be used to predict attributes of designs	Looking for regularity and using patterns to make predictions (all *Connected Mathematics* units)	Making inferences and predictions based on observation and proving predictions (high school)
Relating rigid motions to the concept of symmetry Relating rigid motions to the congruence of figures	Relating similarity transformations to the concept of similarity (*Stretching and Shrinking*)	Describing symmetry in graphs, such as graphs of quadratic functions, periodic functions, and power functions (high school)
Using symmetry and congruence to reason about figures	Performing and analyzing similarity transformations (*Stretching and Shrinking*)	Finding equations for circles and points on circles (*The Shapes of Algebra*) Reasoning about congruence theorems in geometry (high school)
Describing rigid motions in words and with coordinate rules	Describing similarity transformations in words and with coordinate rules (*Stretching and Shrinking*)	Using matrices to represent transformations (high school)

Planning for the Unit

Pacing Suggestions and Materials

Investigations and Assessments	Pacing 45–50 min. classes	Materials for Students	Materials for Teachers
1 Three Types of Symmetry	4 days	Labsheets 1.1A, 1.1B, 1.2, 1.3, 1.4, 1ACE Exercises 2–9, 18–25, 28–30, 46, 50–53, 55, 57	Transparencies 1.1A–C, 1.2, 1.3, 1.4A–C
Mathematical Reflections	$\frac{1}{2}$ day		
Assessment: Check Up 1	$\frac{1}{2}$ day		
2 Symmetry Transformations	5 days	Labsheets 2.1A–C, 2.2A, 2.2B, 2.3A, 2.3B, 2.4A, 2.4B, 2ACE Exercises 1–15, 30, 31, 33	Transparencies 2.1A, 2.1B, 2.2A, 2.2B, 2.3A, 2.3B, 2.4A, 2.4B
Mathematical Reflections	$\frac{1}{2}$ day		
3 Exploring Congruence	5 days	Labsheets 3.1, 3.2, 3.3, 3.4A, 3.4B, 3ACE Exercises 1–4	Chart paper, Transparencies 3.1A, 3.1B, 3.2, 3.3A, 3.3B, 3.4, copy of turtle on transparency paper that can be moved around
Mathematical Reflections	$\frac{1}{2}$ day		
Assessment: Partner Quiz	1 day		
4 Applying Congruence and Symmetry	3 days	Labsheets 4.1, 4.2A, 4.2B, 4ACE Exercise 8	Transparencies 4.1, 4.2A, 4.2B
Mathematical Reflections	$\frac{1}{2}$ day		
Assessment: Check Up 2	$\frac{1}{2}$ day		
5 Transforming Coordinates	4 days	Labsheets 5.1A, 5.1B, 5.2A–C, 5.3, 5.4, 5ACE Exercises 1–3, 5–15, 23	Transparencies 5.1A–C, 5.2A, 5.2B, 5.3A 5.3B, 5.4
Mathematical Reflections	$\frac{1}{2}$ day		
Looking Back and Looking Ahead	1 day		Transparencies LBLA A–C
Assessment: Self Assessment	Take Home		
Assessment: Unit Test	1 day		

Total Time $27\frac{1}{2}$ days

For detailed pacing for Problems within each Investigation, see the Suggested Pacing at the beginning of each Investigation.

For pacing with block scheduling, see next page.

Materials to Use in All Investigations

Graphing calculators, blank transparencies and transparency markers (optional), student notebooks, tracing paper (or lightweight plain paper), rulers, mirrors, transparent reflection tools, angle rulers or protractors	Blank transparencies and transparency markers (optional), overhead graphning calculator (optional)

Pacing for Block Scheduling (90-minute class periods)

Investigation	Suggested Pacing	Investigation	Suggested Pacing	Investigation	Suggested Pacing
Investigation 1	**$2\frac{1}{2}$ days**	**Investigation 3**	**3 days**	**Investigation 5**	**$2\frac{1}{2}$ days**
Problem 1.1	$\frac{1}{2}$ day	Problem 3.1	$\frac{1}{2}$ day	Problem 5.1	$\frac{1}{2}$ day
Problem 1.2	$\frac{1}{2}$ day	Problem 3.2	$\frac{1}{2}$ day	Problem 5.2	$\frac{1}{2}$ day
Problem 1.3	$\frac{1}{2}$ day	Problem 3.3	1 day	Problem 5.3	$\frac{1}{2}$ day
Problem 1.4	$\frac{1}{2}$ day	Problem 3.4	$\frac{1}{2}$ day	Problem 5.4	$\frac{1}{2}$ day
Math Reflections	$\frac{1}{2}$ day	Math Reflections	$\frac{1}{2}$ day	Math Reflections	$\frac{1}{2}$ day
Investigation 2	**3 days**	**Investigation 4**	**2 days**		
Problem 2.1	$\frac{1}{2}$ day	Problem 4.1	$\frac{1}{2}$ day		
Problem 2.2	1 day	Problem 4.2	1 day		
Problem 2.3	$\frac{1}{2}$ day	Math Reflections	$\frac{1}{2}$ day		
Problem 2.4	$\frac{1}{2}$ day				
Math Reflections	$\frac{1}{2}$ day				

Vocabulary

Essential Terms Developed in This Unit		Useful Terms Referenced in This Unit	Terms Developed in Previous Units
Angle of rotation	Rotation symmetry	Angle of rotation	Diagonal
Basic design element	Symmetry	Center of rotation	Equilateral triangle
Congruent	Tessellation	Direction of translation	Hexagon
Congruent figures	Transformation	Image	Parallel
Line reflection	Translation	Kaleidoscope	Parallelogram
Line of symmetry	Translation symmetry	Mirror symmetry	Perpendicular
Reflection		Reflection line	Quadrilateral
Reflection symmetry		Strip pattern	Transformation
Rotation			Tessellation

Program Resources

For: Teacher Resources
Web Code: apk-5500

Components

Use the chart below to quickly see which components are available for each Investigation.

Invest.	Labsheets	Additional Practice	Transparencies		Formal Assessment		Assessment Options	
			Problem	Summary	Check Up	Partner Quiz	Multiple-Choice	Question Bank
1	1.1A, 1.1B, 1.2, 1.3, 1.4, 1ACE Exercises 2–9, 18–25, 28–30, 46, 50–53, 55, 57	✔	1.1A–C, 1.2, 1.3, 1.4A–C		✔		✔	✔
2	2.1A–C, 2.2A, 2.2B, 2.3A, 2.3B, 2.4A, 2.4B, 2ACE Exercises 1–15, 30, 31, 33	✔	2.1A, 2.1B, 2.2A, 2.2B, 2.3A, 2.3B, 2.4A, 2.4B				✔	✔
3	3.1, 3.2, 3.3, 3.4A, 3.4B, 3ACE Exercises 1–4	✔	3.1A, 3.1B, 3.2, 3.3A, 3.3B, 3.4			✔	✔	✔
4	4.1, 4.2A, 4.2B, 4ACE Exercise 8	✔	4.1, 4.2A, 4.2B		✔		✔	
5	5.1A, 5.1B, 5.2A, 5.2B, 5.2C, 5.3, 5.4, 5ACE Exercises 1–3, 5–15, 23	✔	5.1A–C, 5.2A, 5.2B, 5.3A, 5.3B, 5.4				✔	✔
For the Unit		*ExamView* CD-ROM, Web site	LBLA A–C		Unit Test, Notebook Check, Self Assessment		Multiple-Choice, Question Bank, *ExamView* CD-ROM	

Also Available For Use With This Unit

- Parent Guide: take-home letter for the unit
- Implementing CMP

- Spanish Assessment Resources
- Additional online and technology resources

Technology

The Use of Calculators

Connected Mathematics was developed with the belief that calculators should always be available and that students should decide when to use them.

If your students have access to computers, you may want to let them use a geometry or drawing program to explore transformations and tessellations. These programs allow students to apply symmetry transformations to polygons to make tessellating shapes.

Student Activity CD-ROM

Includes interactive activities to enhance the learning in the Problems within Investigations.

PHSchool.com

For Students Multiple-choice practice with instant feedback, updated data sources, data sets for Tinkerplots data software.

For Teachers Professional development, curriculum support, downloadable forms, and more.

See also www.math.msu.edu/cmp for more resources for both teachers and students.

ExamView® CD-ROM

Make multiple versions of practice sheets and tests for course objectives and standardized tests. Includes dynamic questions, online testing, student reports, and all test and practice items in Spanish. Also includes all items in the *Assessment Resources* and *Additional Practice*.

Teacher Express™ CD-ROM

Includes a lesson planning tool, the Teacher's Guide pages, and all the teaching resources.

LessonLab Online Courses

LessonLab offers comprehensive, facilitated professional development designed to help teachers implement CMP2 and improve student achievement. To learn more, please visit PHSchool.com/cmp2.

Assessment Summary

Ongoing Informal Assessment

Embedded in the Student Unit

Problems Use students' work from the Problems to check student understanding.

ACE exercises Use ACE exercises for homework assignments to assess student understanding.

Mathematical Reflections Have students summarize their learning at the end of each Investigation.

Looking Back and Looking Ahead At the end of the unit, use the first two sections to allow students to show what they know about the unit.

Additional Resources

Teacher's Edition Use the Check for Understanding feature of some Summaries and the probing questions that appear in the *Launch, Explore,* or *Summarize* sections of all Investigations to check student understanding.

Self Assessment

Notebook Check Students use this tool to organize and check their notebooks before giving them to their teacher. Located in *Assessment Resources.*

Self Assessment At the end of the unit, students reflect on and provide examples of what they learned. Located in *Assessment Resources.*

Formal Assessment

Choose the assessment materials that are appropriate for your students.

Assessment	For Use After	Focus	Student Work
Check Up 1	Invest. 1	Skills	Individual
Check Up 2	Invest. 4	Skills	Individual
Partner Quiz	Invest. 3	Rich problems	Pair
Unit Test	The Unit	Skills, rich problems	Individual
Unit Project	The Unit	Rich problems	Individual or Group

Additional Resources

Multiple-Choice Items Use these items for homework, review, a quiz, or add them to the Unit Test.

Question Bank Choose from these questions for homework, review, or replacements for Quiz, Check Up, or Unit Test questions.

Additional Practice Choose practice exercises for each investigation for homework, review, or formal assessments.

ExamView **CD-ROM** Make practice sheets, review quizzes, and tests with this dynamic software. Give online tests and receive student progress reports. (All test items available in Spanish.)

Spanish Assessment Resources

Includes Partner Quizzes, Check Ups, Unit Test, Multiple-Choice Items, Question Bank, Notebook Check, and Self Assessment. Plus, the *ExamView* CD-ROM has all test items in Spanish.

Correlation to Standardized Tests

Investigation	NAEP	Terra Nova CAT6	Terra Nova CTBS	ITBS	SAT10	Local Test
1 Three Types of Symmetry	G2c	✔	✔			
2 Symmetry Transformations	G2c	✔	✔			
3 Exploring Congruence	G2e, G2f		✔		✔	
4 Applying Congruence and Symmetry	M1k, G2f		✔		✔	
5 Connecting Transformations to Coordinates	G2c	✔	✔			

NAEP National Assessment of Educational Progress

CAT6/Terra Nova California Achievement Test, 6th Ed.
CTBS/Terra Nova Comprehensive Test of Basic Skills

ITBS Iowa Test of Basic Skills, Form M
SAT10 Stanford Achievement Test, 10th Ed.

Introducing Your Students to *Kaleidoscopes, Hubcaps, and Mirrors*

Students' natural fascination with symmetric patterns is used to introduce this unit.

To find out how much students already know about symmetry, direct their attention to the objects pictured on the opening pages of the student edition. Ask them to look at first the hubcap, then the tessellation, then the kaleidoscope, and then the quilt pattern and to observe how part of the object can be folded, rotated, or slid to match another part. For each object, ask students whether they see other objects—on the page or somewhere in the classroom—that show the same property. Ask them to describe, as clearly as they can, each of the three properties.

Explain to the class that all of these objects have symmetry. You might end by asking, "What do you think the word symmetry means?" and allowing students to share their ideas.

Using the Unit Opener

When students have had a chance to share their ideas on symmetry, move to the three questions posed on the opening pages of the Student Edition. Discuss these briefly with your students and review the Introduction on the next page. The problems will be answered within the unit, so students are not expected to be able to solve them here. The problems serve as an advanced organizer for what the students will encounter and learn to do during the unit. Take a few minutes to allow the sharing of ideas from the students with the goal of generating enthusiasm for the kinds of situations in the unit. This can also give you an informal assessment of where your students are on understanding the meaning of symmetry.

Using the Mathematical Highlights

The Mathematical Highlights page in the Student Edition provides information to students, parents, and other family members. It gives students a preview of the mathematics and some of the overarching questions that they should ask themselves while studying *Kaleidoscopes, Hubcaps, and Mirrors*.

As they work through the unit, students can refer back to the Mathematical Highlights page to review what they have learned and to preview what is still to come. This page also tells students' families what mathematical ideas and activities will be covered as the class works through *Kaleidoscopes, Hubcaps, and Mirrors*.

Using the Unit Project

The optional Unit Project consists of two hands-on activities. Either or both parts of the project will give students an opportunity to apply what they have learned about symmetry.

In Part 1, students make tessellating shapes by applying symmetry transformations to the sides of a square and to the sides of a nonsquare rhombus.

In Part 2, students explore the symmetries of the various shapes appearing in an origami construction.

Each project can be done by students individually, but students will make more discoveries about tessellations and symmetry if they share ideas about their work in groups or as a whole class.

See the Guide to the Unit Project section on page 136 for more information about assigning and assessing the project.

Investigation 1 — Three Types of Symmetry

Mathematical and Problem-Solving Goals

- Understand important properties of symmetry
- Recognize and describe reflection, rotation, and translation symmetry informally
- Use tools, such as tracing paper, to analyze designs to determine their symmetries
- Design shapes that have specified symmetries
- Identify a basic design element that can be used to replicate a design

Mathematics Background

For background on symmetry, see pages 4–10.

Summary of Problems

Problem 1.1 Reflection Symmetry

Students explore ways for checking for reflection symmetry and search for examples of such symmetry in several designs.

Problem 1.2 Rotation Symmetry

Students analyze illustrations of hubcaps, pinwheels, and other designs to explore the properties of rotation symmetry and the concept of angle of rotation.

Problem 1.3 Symmetry in Kaleidoscopes

Students look for reflection and rotation symmetry in various kaleidoscope designs and are introduced to the idea of a basic design element.

Problem 1.4 Translation Symmetry

Students begin to look at strip patterns and wallpaper patterns to understand translation symmetry.

	Suggested Pacing	Materials for Students	Materials for Teachers	ACE Assignments
All	$4\frac{1}{2}$ days	Student notebooks, graphing calculators tracing paper (or lightweight plain paper), grid paper, rulers, mirrors, transparent reflection tools, angle rulers or protractors (1 per group)	Blank transparency and transparency markers (optional), overhead graphing calculator (optional)	
1.1	1 day	Labsheets 1.1A, 1.1B, 1ACE Exercises 2–9 (optional)	Transparencies 1.1A–C	1–9, 31–33
1.2	1 day	Labsheets 1.2, 1ACE Exercises 18, 19 (optional)	Transparency 1.2	10–19, 34–45, 54
1.3	1 day	Labsheets 1.3, 1ACE Exercises 20–25, 46 (optional)	Transparency 1.3	20–25, 46–49
1.4	1 day	Labsheets 1.4, 1ACE Exercises 28–30, 50–53, 55, 57 (optional)	Transparencies 1.4A–C	26–30, 50–53, 55–57
MR	$\frac{1}{2}$ day			

1.1 Reflection Symmetry

Goals

- Understand important properties of symmetry
- Recognize and describe reflection, rotation, and translation symmetry informally
- Use tools, such as tracing paper, to analyze designs to determine their reflection symmetries

Launch 1.1

Review the introduction to reflection, rotation, and translation symmetry that is presented in the student edition. Start with the Getting Ready. Give students a couple of minutes to examine the three pictures and describe what might earn them a symmetry label. Indicate that the Investigation is about the kinds of symmetry exhibited by the three designs.

Discuss with students how they might determine whether reflection symmetry exists in a given design.

Suggested Questions

- *In the first problem you will explore reflection symmetry. What does the word* symmetry *mean to you?*

- *What does the word* reflection *make you think about?*

Display an object or a design that has reflection symmetry, such as the butterfly pictured in the student edition.

- *Does this object have symmetry?*

- *How might you check for reflection symmetry in an object or a design? What tools might be useful?*

Look at the heart picture with the students. Students often recognize that the two halves of a design on either side of a line of symmetry are mirror images, and suggest using a mirror to check for reflection symmetry. If you have mirrors or other reflecting tools available, demonstrate their use for the class. A subtle point to make here with students is that if you place a mirror on any design, the part of the design that is exposed in front of the mirror

together with the image in the mirror will make a design with reflection symmetry. The question is whether this symmetric design looks exactly like the original design. If so the original design has reflection symmetry.

When using a mirror to test for reflection symmetry, it is hard to accurately check the details of the design. It may be difficult to determine whether a reflected image exactly matches the design behind the mirror, since that part of the design is not visible.

Transparent reflection tools, such as Image Reflectors, allow the viewer to see a reflected image while simultaneously looking at the object through the transparent plastic. This helps the user to match the reflected image with the part of the design being the plastic. When the two halves match, the line of symmetry can be identified by drawing a line segment along the bottom edge of the plastic.

Encourage students to think about other ways they might check for reflection symmetry.

Suggested Questions

- *What other methods or procedures can you think of for testing whether a design has reflection symmetry?*

- *How might you use tracing paper to find reflection symmetry?*

Have mirrors, transparent reflection tools, tracing paper, rulers, and other materials available for students to use. Distribute Labsheets 1.1A and 1.1B to each student.

Have students work individually and then share their work with a group of three or four.

Explore 1.1

Encourage students to be accurate as they draw each line of symmetry. Make sure they understand that the problem asks about the symmetry of the entire design, not of individual elements of the design such as a triangle, square, cross, or diamond.

As you circulate, ask students to think about which tools or methods are the most useful or the easiest for working with the designs in this problem.

Have students share their answers with the class, perhaps drawing each line of symmetry on Transparencies 1.1A and 1.1B on the overhead. Encourage them to be precise as they explain their reasoning and how they used specific tools or methods to check for reflection symmetry.

At first glance, it may appear that the design in Question C has two lines of symmetry in addition to the horizontal and vertical lines through the center: those on the diagonals. However, the orientation of the eight small triangles makes these possible lines of symmetry incorrect. Such a fine detail can easily be overlooked in checking for reflection symmetry. Explore this idea with the class.

Suggested Questions

- *What is it about the small triangles that makes a diagonal line of symmetry incorrect?* (Student responses should include language about the 'way the triangle is turned', which foreshadows the language of rotation transformations.)

- *What could we do to make this design have four lines of symmetry?*

Three of many ways to make this design symmetrical about its diagonals are to remove the small triangles, to make the triangles into diamonds, or to rotate the triangles.

The design in Question D has no reflection symmetry. Ask the students whether the figure would demonstrate reflection symmetry if the feet, head, and arms were removed. The answer is still no because the patterns in the upper-right and upper-left corners are not mirror images.

Questions E, F, G, and H move the discussion of reflection symmetry to polygons. You want students to generalize that non-square rectangles have exactly two lines of symmetry; garden variety parallelograms (no right angles and not all sides of equal length) have no line symmetry; all equilateral triangles have three lines of symmetry; and isosceles triangles (with exactly two sides equal) have only one line of symmetry.

Review with the class the various tools they used in this problem.

Suggested Question

- *How can you use tracing paper to test a design for reflection symmetry?* (Trace the entire design, and look for a way to fold the tracing so that one half folds onto the other half. The fold line is the line of symmetry. Or, mark where the proposed line of symmetry is, trace the half of the design on one side of that line, and then flip the traced half over the line to see whether it matches the other half.)

If students have used transparent reflection tools, ask how they can be used to test a design for reflection symmetry. Students should be able to explain that they set the tool on what appears to be the line of symmetry and then observe whether the two halves of the figure match.

1.1 Reflection Symmetry

Mathematical Goals

- Understand important properties of symmetry
- Recognize and describe reflection, rotation, and translation symmetry informally
- Use tools, such as tracing paper, to analyze designs to determine their reflection symmetries

Launch

Review the introduction to reflection, rotation, and translation symmetry that is presented in the student edition. Start with the Getting Ready challenge. Give students a couple of minutes to examine the three pictures and describe what might earn them a symmetry label. Indicate that the Investigation is about the kinds of symmetry exhibited by the three designs.

- *In the first problem you will explore reflection symmetry. What does the word* symmetry *mean to you? What does the word* reflection *make you think about?*

Display an object or a design that has reflection symmetry, such as the butterfly pictured in the student edition.

- *Does this object have symmetry? How might you check for reflection symmetry in an object or a design?*

Have students work individually and then share their work with a group of three or four.

Materials

- Transparencies 1.1A–C
- Mirrors or transparent reflecting tools
- Rules, angle rulers, or protractors
- Tracing paper

Explore

Encourage students to be accurate as they draw each line of symmetry. Make sure they understand that the problem asks about the symmetry of the entire design, not of individual elements of the design such as a triangle, square, cross, or diamond. As you circulate, ask students to think about which tools or methods are the most useful or the easiest for working with the designs in this problem.

Materials

- Labsheets 1.1A, 1.1B

Summarize

Have students share their answers with the class, drawing each line of symmetry on Transparency 1.1 on the overhead. Encourage them to be precise as they explain their reasoning. In Question C, ask:

- *What is it about the small triangles that makes a diagonal line of symmetry incorrect?*
- *What could we do to make this design have four lines of symmetry?*
- *How can you use tracing paper to test for reflection symmetry?*

Materials

- Student notebooks
- Labsheets 1ACE Exercises 2–9 (optional)

Vocabulary

- symmetry
- line symmetry
- line of symmetry
- reflection symmetry

ACE Assignment Guide for Problem 1.1

Differentiated Instruction
Solutions for All Learners

Core 1–9

Other *Connections* 31–33; unassigned choices from previous problems

Labsheets 1ACE Exercises 2–5 and 1ACE Exercises 6–9 are provided if Exercises 2–9 are assigned

Adapted For suggestions about adapting ACE exercises, see the CMP *Special Needs Handbook*.

Answers to Problem 1.1

A. Only one line of symmetry, vertical through the middle of the figure.

B. Two lines of symmetry, vertical and horizontal through the center of the figure.

C. Two lines of symmetry, vertical and horizontal (at first, it might look like diagonals are also lines of symmetry, but the orientation of the small triangles precludes this).

D. No lines of symmetry.

E. 2   **F.** 0   **G.** 3   **H.** 1

1.2 Rotation Symmetry

Goals

- Recognize and describe rotation symmetry, including the center of rotation and the angle of rotation

- Use tools, such as angle rulers and compasses, to analyze designs to determine their rotation symmetries

- Design shapes that have specified symmetries

Launch 1.2

Have students look at the picture of the pinwheel design in the introduction to the problem. Discuss the fact that although the pinwheel does not have reflection symmetry (students can verify this using tracing paper or transparent reflection tools), it does have another type of symmetry, rotation symmetry.

Objects that rotate around a center point are often designed so that after a partial turn, they look the same as they did in the original position.

Suggested Question

- *What tools might be useful for checking whether the pinwheel has rotation symmetry?*

Some students might suggest sketching the pinwheel on tracing paper or a blank transparency and then rotating the sketch about the center until the sketch again coincides with the original.

There are many angles through which we can rotate this pinwheel about its center point so that it looks the same as it does in its original position. The smallest angle through which the copy can be turned to coincide with the original is called the *angle of rotation.*

Have mirrors, tracing paper, rulers, angle rulers or protractors, and other tools available. Have students work individually on the problem and then check their ideas with their partners.

Explore 1.2

Students can measure the angle of rotation in the pinwheel in a number of ways. For example, the 45° angle of rotation might be measured by

locating the center point and then drawing lines from the center point to corresponding points of two adjacent parts of the pattern.

The basic idea is to determine "a sector," or section, of the pinwheel that could be copied and rotated several times to make the entire pinwheel design. The angle of the section is the angle of rotation. See the examples of three ways to determine the angle of rotation in the hubcap designs below.

If students find determining the angles of rotation for the pinwheel and the other designs easy, ask:

Suggested Question

- *Can you think of a way to determine the angle of rotation without using a measuring tool?*

This idea will be explored in the summary. Have students who finish early make their own designs with rotation symmetry.

Ask students to share the methods they used to determine the angle of rotation for the pinwheel and then the other designs. Some will talk about drawing lines from the center of the design to corresponding points of two adjacent parts of the pattern, thus making an angle that can be measured with an angle ruler or a protractor. Help students to understand that each design has a particular angle of rotation regardless of which two adjacent parts are chosen.

Informally explore finding the center of rotation.

Suggested Question

- *How would you find the point around which the figure is rotated if you need its location to be exact?* (Students may suggest guess and check as a method. Finding the center of rotation will be discussed further in Investigation 2.)

Invite students to share their answers to Question D, either drawing the designs on the board or on a transparency. Ask how the students determined that their designs had rotation symmetry but no reflection symmetry.

Next, lead the class in an exploration of the relationship between the angle of rotation and the number of ways a particular design can be oriented to coincide with the original.

Suggested Question

- *Is there a way to determine the angle of rotation for a particular design without actually measuring it?*

Choose one of the designs as an example. If you choose the hubcap, looking for the smallest section of the hubcap that can be rotated to get the complete hubcap is a way to determine the angle of rotation without measuring. In hubcap 1, one fifth of the hubcap can be replicated five times to complete the design. The angle of rotation is $360° ÷ 5 = 72°$.

If no ideas are offered, point out the patterns in the pictures in Problem 1.2. You might choose to focus on the hubcaps.

Suggested Questions

- *In one full rotation of hubcap 1, how many times could you stop and have the hubcap look the same as it does now?* (5 times) *What is the angle of rotation for this hubcap?* (72°) *What's the measure of a full turn?* (360°)

- *In one full rotation of hubcap 2, how many times could you stop and have the hubcap look the same as it does now?* (3 times) *What is the angle of rotation for this hubcap?* (120°) *What's the measure of a full turn?* (360°)

- *What relationship do you see between the angle of rotation, the number of ways you could match the original design in a full rotation and the measure of a full turn?* (The angle of rotation is the measure of a full turn divided by the number of ways to match the design: $360° ÷ 3 = 120°$ and $360° ÷ 5 = 72°$.)

If students are having trouble understanding this relationship, you may also want to try this for some of the other designs. Once students understand this relationship, have them apply it.

- *Suppose you know the angle of rotation of a particular design. How can you use it to find all the other angles through which the design can be rotated to match the original design? We call these rotation symmetries.*

You may want to use an example, such as the star shown below, to demonstrate this idea. The star has an angle of rotation of $360° ÷ 6 = 60°$. The possible angles through which it can be rotated to coincide with the original design are $1 × 60°, 2 × 60°, 3 × 60°, 4 × 60°, 5 × 60°$, and $6 × 60°$; in other words, 60°, 120°, 180°, 240°, 300°, and a full rotation of 360°.

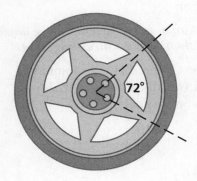

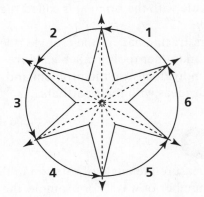

1.2 Rotation Symmetry

Mathematical Goals

- Recognize and describe rotation symmetry, including the center of rotation and the angle of rotation
- Use tools, such as angle rulers and compasses, to analyze designs to determine their rotation symmetries
- Design shapes that have specified symmetries

Launch

Have students look at the picture of the pinwheel design in the introduction to the problem. Discuss the fact that although the pinwheel does not have reflection symmetry, it does have another type of symmetry, rotation symmetry.

- *What tools might be useful for checking whether the pinwheel has rotation symmetry?*

Have students work individually and then share their work with a group of three or four.

Materials
- Transparency 1.2
- Mirrors or transparent reflecting tools
- Rules, angle, rulers, or protractors
- Tracing paper

Explore

Students can measure the angle of rotation in the pinwheel in a number of ways. For example, the 45° angle of rotation might be measured by locating the center point and then drawing lines from the center point to corresponding points of two adjacent parts of the pattern.

- *Can you think of a way to determine the angle of rotation without using a measuring tool?*

Materials
- Labsheet 1.2

Summarize

Ask students to share the methods they used to determine the angle of rotation. Encourage them to think about how to determine the angle of rotation without measuring.

- *In one full rotation of hubcap 1, how many times could you stop and have the hubcap look the same as it does now?*
- *What is the angle of rotation for this hubcap? What's the measure of a full turn?*
- *How can you use the angle of rotation to find all the other angles through which the design can be rotated to match the original design?*

Materials
- Student notebooks
- Labsheet 1ACE Exercises 18, 19

Vocabulary
- rotation
- rotation symmetry
- angle of rotation
- center of rotation

ACE Assignment Guide for Problem 1.2

Core 10–17, 34–40
Other *Applications* 18, 19; *Connections* 41–45; *Extensions* 54; unassigned choices from previous problems

Labsheets 1ACE Exercises 18–19 are provided if Exercises 18–19 are assigned

Adapted For suggestions about adapting Exercise 17 and other ACE exercises, see the CMP *Special Needs Handbook.*
Connecting to Prior Units 34–40: *Shapes and Designs*

Answers to Problem 1.2

A. Any multiple of 45 degrees; the angle of rotation is 45 degrees.

B. 1. 90°, 180°, 270°, angle of rotation is 90°.

2. 60°, 120°, 180°, 240°, 300° angle of rotation is 60°.

3. 30°, 60°, 90°, 120°, 150°, 180°, 210°, 240°, 270°, 300°, 330°, angle of rotation is 30°.

C. The angle of rotation is always the smallest rotation that will make the copy coincide with the original design. The other rotation symmetries are multiples of this. For example, if the angle of rotation is 60° then 1(60°), 2(60°), 3(60°), 4(60°), and 5(60°) are all rotation symmetries.

D. 1. Hubcap 1 can be rotated through any multiple of 72°, and Hubcap 2 can be turned through any multiple of 120°. The center of rotation is directly in the center of each circle in the hubcaps.

2. Hubcap 1 has 5 lines of symmetry (see picture below) while hubcap 2 has none.

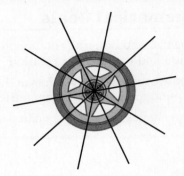

E. Answers will vary. One possible answer:

F. Answers will vary. One possible answer:

G. A rectangle and a parallelogram have 180° rotation symmetry around the point of intersection of the diagonals. A square has 90° rotation symmetry.

1.3 Symmetry in Kaleidoscope Designs

Goals

- Find and describe reflection and rotation symmetries in kaleidoscope designs

- Make designs that have certain combinations of reflection and rotation symmetries

- Identify a basic design element that can be used to replicate a design.

Launch 1.3

Direct students' attention to the kaleidoscope designs pictured in the student edition before the problem.

Suggested Questions

- *What basic polygon shape do these designs have?* (A hexagon)

- *Do you see any reflection symmetry in these designs?* (Yes—most of the designs seem to have reflection symmetry.)

- *Do you see any rotation symmetry in some these designs?* (Yes—all the designs seem to have rotation symmetry.)

Have mirrors, transparent reflecting tools, tracing paper, rulers, angle rulers or protractors, and other tools available for students to use. Have students work in pairs to do the problem.

Explore 1.3

Students are asked to look for reflection and rotation symmetry in each design. If they have difficulty identifying all the symmetries in the designs, encourage them to use the various tools and techniques they have experimented with in the previous problems.

Suggested Question

- *How is the rotation symmetry of a design related to the rotation symmetries of a hexagon?* (Each of the rotation symmetries of one of the designs is also a rotation symmetry for the hexagon.)

Summarize 1.3

Have students share the reflection and rotation symmetries they found in each design. Then help them to make some general observations about the kaleidoscope designs.

Suggested Questions

- *What do you notice about the angles of rotation for these designs?* (Each design has an angle of rotation of either 60° or 120° but not both.)

- *What similarities and differences did you notice among the designs?* (All the designs have six triangular parts. Some of the designs have 60° angles of rotation and others have 120°.)

- *How can you explain the similarities and differences?* (The designs are based on hexagons, and regular hexagons have 60° angles of rotation. In some of the designs, the six triangular sections are all identical, so those designs have 60° angles of rotation. In others, there are two different triangular sections, or one triangle is the reflection of another. Those designs must be rotated through two triangular sections, or 120°.)

Have students share the various basic design elements they found for the designs.

Have a student put up a table showing the number of lines of symmetry and the smallest rotation symmetry turn. You may want to go over the table with the students.

Suggested Questions

- *What mathematical relationship do you see between the number of lines of symmetry and the angle of rotation?* (The product of these two numbers is always 360°.)

1.3 Symmetry in Kaleidoscope Designs

Mathematical Goals

- Find and describe reflection and rotation symmetries in kaleidoscope designs
- Make designs that have certain combinations of reflection and rotation symmetries
- Identify a basic design element that can be used to replicate a design.

Launch

Direct students' attention to the kaleidoscope designs pictured in the student edition before the problem.

- *What basic polygon shape do these designs have?*
- *Do you see any reflection symmetry in these designs? Do you see any rotation symmetry in some of these designs?*

Have students work in pairs to do the problem.

Materials

- Transparency 1.3
- Mirrors or transparent reflecting tools
- Rules, angle, rulers, or protractors
- Tracing paper

Explore

If they have difficulty identifying all the symmetries in the designs, encourage them to use the various tools and techniques they have experimented with in the previous problems.

- *How is the rotation symmetry of a design related to the rotation symmetries of a regular hexagon?*

Materials

- Labsheet 1.3

Summarize

Have students share the reflection and rotation symmetries they found in each design.

- *What do you notice about the angles of rotation for these designs?*
- *What similarities and differences did you notice among the designs?*
- *How can you explain the similarities and differences?*

Have students share their basic design elements. Have a student put up a table showing the number of lines of symmetry and the smallest rotation symmetry turn.

- *What mathematical relationship do you see between the number of lines of symmetry and the angle of rotation?*

Materials

- Student notebooks
- Labsheets 1ACE Exercises 20–25, 46 (optional)

Vocabulary

- basic design element
- kaleidoscope

ACE Assignment Guide for Problem 1.3

Core 20–25, 46

Other *Connections,* 47–49; unassigned choices from previous problems

Labsheets 1ACE Exercises 20–23, 1ACE Exercises 24–25, and 1ACE Exercise 46 are provided if Exercises 20–25 and 46 are assigned

Adapted For suggestions about adapting ACE exercises, see the CMP *Special Needs Handbook.*
Connecting to Prior Units 47–49: *Filling and Wrapping*

Answers to Problem 1.3

A. and B.

Since all figures are outlined by regular hexagons, the line symmetries must be either on diagonals joining opposite vertices or the midpoints of opposite sides and the rotations must be some multiple of 60°. The patterns for each design are as follows:

Design A: Line symmetry across any diagonal; rotation of only multiples of 120° about the center.

Design B: Line symmetry across any diagonal; rotation of only multiples of 120° about the center.

Design C: No lines of symmetry; rotation of only multiples of 120° about the center—this one is not a kaleidoscope design.

Design D: Line symmetry across any diagonal and any line connecting midpoints of opposite sides. Rotation of any multiple of 60°.

Design E: Same as Design B.

Design F: Line symmetry across any diagonal; rotation of only multiples of 120°.

C. 1.

Design	Lines of Symmetry	Angle of Rotation
A	6	60°
B	3	120°
C	0	120°
D	6	60°
E	3	120°
F	6	60°

2. Excluding design 3, which has no lines of symmetry, the product of the number of lines of symmetry and the angle of rotation is always 360°.

3. There are three lines of symmetry and the angle of rotation is 120°. The design fits the relationship.

D. The basic design element is a sector of the hexagon with central angle equal to the smallest rotation possible.

E. The third is not a kaleidoscope design since it has no reflection symmetries.

Translation Symmetry

Goals

- Recognize and describe translation symmetry

- Use tools, such as tracing paper, transparency paper, or rulers, to analyze designs to determine their translation symmetries

- Design shapes that have specified symmetries

- Identify a basic design element that can be used to replicate a design

Launch 1.4

Talk about the Getting Ready with the students. One of the interesting aspects of this is the importance of the infinite: that if we move a finite strip pattern or piece of patterned wallpaper, anyone could tell. But with an infinite strip pattern, you could slide the whole design a certain distance and no one would be able to tell that it had been moved.

Look at the examples of strip patterns in the student edition. A strip pattern is made by drawing and moving. After you draw the original design element, you slide your pen to a new position and repeat your drawing. Then you slide the same distance and direction to a new position, repeat the drawing, and keep going in the same way. These slide movements are called translations.

You may want to illustrate this process with the idea of making a stamp of a basic design element and using that stamp repeatedly to make a pattern with translation symmetry. You might even demonstrate with a real stamp.

View the wallpaper pattern in the student edition.

Suggested Questions

- *How would you give directions to make the wallpaper pattern?*

Students may informally describe the motion, for example, as "move to the right and make a copy of the original piece."

- *Would your directions be precise enough for someone to remake this pattern exactly?* (You would need a distance to translate as well as a direction.)

Have the students work on these problems individually and then compare their answers in groups of three or four.

Explore 1.4

As they work, you may want to remind students that the image in Question B is just a part of an infinite design. The design is meant to cover the plane that extends infinitely in all directions. Each student should produce his or her own results and then compare them with the others produced by the group.

In Question B, advise students to be careful when outlining what they think is the basic design element and specifying a translation that could be used with that element to help make the design. If some students are outlining an element that isn't a basic design element, you might ask:

Suggested Questions

- *Is there anything simpler that would work? Could you simplify your design element?*

- *Are you sure your element would cover the plane with no holes or overlaps?*

Some students may find it easier to trace the basic design elements than to outline them. Also, you may want to distribute blank transparencies so that each group can outline what they have found to be the basic design elements for sharing in the summary.

Ask a student to share the strip pattern he or she made with the basic design element in Question A.

Suggested Questions

- *Does this pattern have rotation or reflection symmetry? Why or why not?*

In Question B, encourage students to share the various ways that they identified the basic design element for the design and specified the translation for each basic design element. It is extremely powerful for them to see that there are many correct ways to specify design elements and translations for each tessellation.

Call on a group to show a basic design element at the overhead.

- *Do you all agree that this basic design element can be used to reproduce the design? Why or why not?*

- *Let's collect every possible way you can think of to specify translations that will remake this design*

Collect as many examples as the class offers in a few minutes.

- *Do you think these are the only directions we could give that would help someone remake this design? (There are many.)*

1.4 Translation Symmetry

Mathematical Goals

- Recognize and describe translation symmetry
- Use tools, such as tracing paper, transparency paper, or rulers, to analyze designs to determine their translation symmetries
- Design shapes that have specified symmetries
- Identify basic design elements that can be used to replicate a design

Launch

Talk about the Getting Ready with the students.

Look at the examples of strip patterns in the student edition. A strip pattern is made by "drawing and moving." After you draw the original design element, you slide your pen to a new position and repeat your drawing.

Look at the wallpaper pattern in the student edition.

- *How would you give directions to make the wallpaper pattern?*

Students may informally describe the motion as "move to the right and make a copy of the original piece."

- *Would your directions be precise enough for someone to remake this pattern exactly?*

Have the students work on these problems individually and then compare their answers in groups of three or four.

Materials
- Transparency 1.4A–C
- Tracing paper
- Mirrors or transparent reflecting tools
- Rules, angle rulers, or protractors

Explore

In Question B, advise students to be careful when outlining what they think is the basic design element and specifying a translation that could be used with that element to help make the design. If some students are outlining an element that isn't a basic design element, you might ask:

- *Is there anything simpler that would work?*
- *Could you simplify your design element?*
- *Would your element cover the plane with no holes or overlaps?*

Materials
- Labsheet 1.4

Summarize

Ask a student to share the strip pattern he or she made with the basic design element in Question A.

- *Does this pattern have rotation or reflection symmetry? Why or why not?*

Call on a group to show a basic design element at the overhead. Ask:

- *Do you all agree that this basic design element can be used to reproduce the design? Why or why not?*
- *Let's collect every possible way you can think of to specify translations that will remake this design.*

Materials
- Student notebooks
- Labsheets 1ACE Exercises 28–30, 50–53, 55, 57

Vocabulary
- translation
- translation symmetry

continued on next page

● *Do you think these are the only directions we could give that would help someone remake this design?*

- magnitude and direction of translation
- translation image

ACE Assignment Guide for Problem 1.4

Differentiated Instruction
Solutions for All Learners

Core 26–30
Other *Connections* 50–53; *Extensions* 55–57; unassigned choices from previous problems

Labsheets for 1ACE Exercises 28–30, 50–53, 55, and 57 are provided if Exercises 28–30, 50–53, 55, and 57 are assigned

Adapted For suggestions about adapting ACE exercises, see the CMP *Special Needs Handbook*.

Answers to Problem 1.4

A. Answers may vary. The most common pattern will likely be what is shown below. (Figure 1)

B. 1. Some possible basic design elements are shown below. The first three are basic design elements with no overlap. The one on the left is just the boxed in portion where the vertices of the box occur at the midpoint of the lines they are on. The middle design (or right design) makes the wallpaper design by moving it first diagonally up or down in the direction of one of the two line segments and then taking the whole strip you make and moving that strip diagonally the other way in the direction of the other line segment.

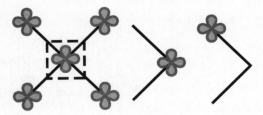

The basic design element shown below overlaps edges when it is translated to make the wallpaper design. **Note:** The important characteristic of wallpaper designs is that they can be made by translating a basic design element. Whether the design overlaps or not is not essential for student understanding of this concept. If students make design elements which overlap, accept them and suggest they search for others that don't overlap.

2. Some possible directions using the design element outlined below:

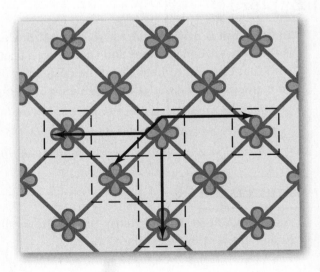

Figure 1

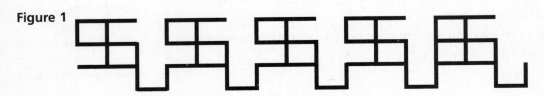

Investigation 1

ACE Assignment Choices

Differentiated Instruction
Solutions for All Learners

Problem 1.1
Core 1–9
Other *Connections* 31–33; unassigned choices from previous problems

Problem 1.2
Core 10–17, 34–40
Other *Applications* 18, 19; *Connections* 41–45; *Extensions* 54; unassigned choices from previous problems

Problem 1.3
Core 20–25, 46
Other *Connections* 47–49; unassigned choices from previous problems

Problem 1.4
Core 26–30
Other *Connections* 50–53; *Extensions* 55–57; unassigned choices from previous problems

Adapted For suggestions about adapting Exercise 17 and other ACE exercises, see the CMP *Special Needs Handbook*.
Connecting to Prior Units 34–40: *Shapes and Designs*; 47–49: *Filling and Wrapping*

Applications

1.

Note: The O has infinite lines of symmetry.

2. Yes; there are 18 lines of symmetry; 9 each of two types. A sample of each type is shown:

3. Yes; there are 4 lines of symmetry:

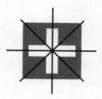

4. No; the design does not have lines of symmetry

5. No; the design does not have lines of symmetry

6. There are 4 lines of symmetry:

7. There are 5 lines of symmetry:

8. No; the design does not have lines of symmetry

9. There are 4 lines of symmetry:

10. The angles of rotation for each are:
   (Exercise 2) 20° and all multiples of 20°
   (Exercise 3) 90° and all multiples of 90°
   (Exercise 6) 90° and all multiples of 90°
   (Exercise 7) 72° and all multiples of 72°
   (Exercise 9) 90° and all multiples of 90°

11. The angles of rotation are all 180°.

H I N O S X Z

Depending on how they are written, X and O may have more rotation symmetries.

12.   90°

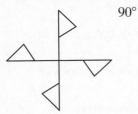

13.   60°

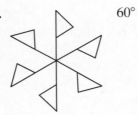

14.   45°

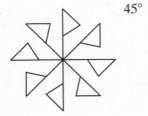

15. a. 72°
   b. Check students' drawings. There are 5 lines of symmetry.

16. Possible answer (the hubcap below has an angle of rotation of 120° and 3 lines of reflection):

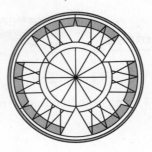

17. B (The pentagon has rotation symmetry 72° about its center. The circle has rotation symmetry. The center of the circle is its center of rotation. The rhombus has 180° rotation symmetry about its center which is marked in the diagram below. The center of rotation is located where the diagonals of this quadrilateral meet.)

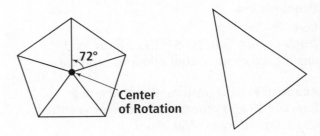

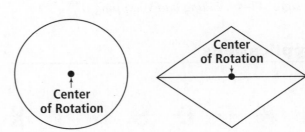

18. Rotation symmetry with a smallest turn of 180°. No reflection symmetry.

19. Rotation symmetry with a smallest turn of 90°. No reflection symmetry.

20.

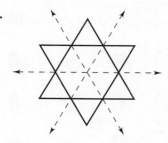

21.

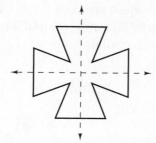

22.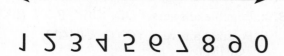

23. 1 2 3 4 5 6 7 8 9 0

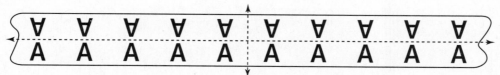

24. This design has 3 lines of symmetry (through the vertices of the hexagon) and rotation symmetry with a smallest turn of 120°.

25. This design has 6 lines of symmetry (3 going through the vertices and 3 going through the midpoints of opposite sides) and rotation symmetry with a smallest turn of 60°.

26. Answers will vary. Check to be sure the symmetries are correct.

    a. One possible strip pattern: (Figure 2)

    b. One possible strip pattern: (Figure 3)

27. a. Answers will vary. Check to be sure the symmetries are correct. One possible wallpaper pattern is shown below.

    b. Possible wallpaper design with some possible translation arrows:

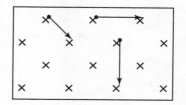

c.

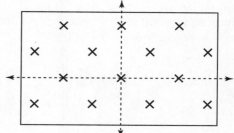

d. Note: Depending on how students make the X and how they create the pattern, the finished design may have an angle of rotation of either 90° or 180°.

Figure 2

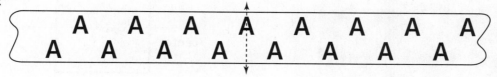

Figure 3

28. The basic design is one of the following:

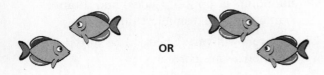

OR

The basic element can be copied and translated in the direction of the arrows shown.

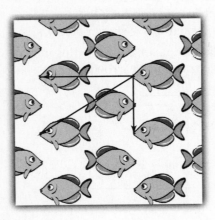

29. There are several sets of basic design elements. Here is an example of one set.

The basic element can be copied and translated in the direction of the arrows below.

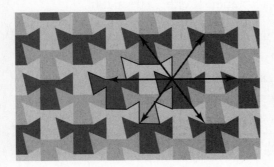

30. The basic design element can be a combination of four differently colored hands oriented horizontally or diagonally.

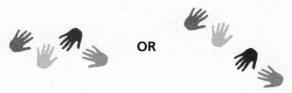

OR

The basic element can be copied and translated in the direction of the arrows below.

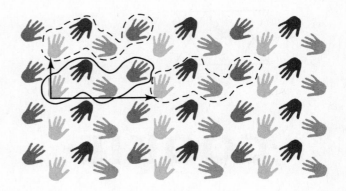

Connections

31. OHIO

32. HAWAII, IOWA, OHIO, UTAH

33. a. Possible answers: COD, KICK, BOX, HIKE

    b. Possible answers: YOYO, WHAM, TOMMY

34. A square has 4 reflection symmetry lines. A square has an angle of rotation of 90°. The center of rotation is located below.

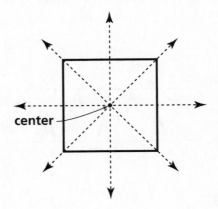

center

35. A non-square rectangle has 2 reflection symmetry lines. A non-square rectangle has angle of rotation of 180°. The center of rotation is located below.

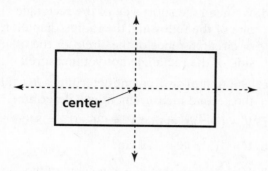

36. A non-rectangular parallelogram has no reflection symmetry. A non-rectangular parallelogram has angle of rotation of 180°. The center of rotation is located below and is located where the diagonals of the parallelogram intersect.

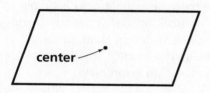

37. An isosceles triangle has one line of reflection symmetry and no rotation symmetry.

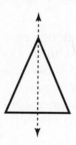

38. An equilateral triangle has 3 lines of reflection symmetry and angle of rotation of 120°. The center of rotation is shown below.

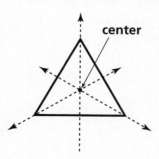

39. The rhombus below has 2 lines of symmetry and angle of rotation of 180°. The center of rotation is shown below.

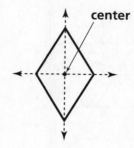

40. An isosceles trapezoid has one line of symmetry and no rotation symmetry.

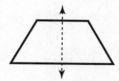

41. *Zane* has reflection symmetry with a vertical line of symmetry between the a and the n.

42. *Yvette* has reflection symmetry with a vertical line of symmetry through the center of the letters.

43. *Eve* has reflection symmetry with a vertical line of symmetry through the center of the V.

44. *Quincy* has rotation symmetry with a center of rotation in the middle of the design and a 180° angle of rotation.

45. *Michael* has rotation symmetry with a center of rotation in the middle of the design and a 180° angle of rotation.

46. The following are 3 possible kaleidoscope designs, depending on which vertex is chosen for the center of the design.

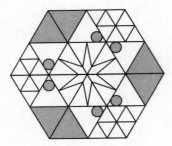

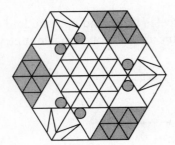

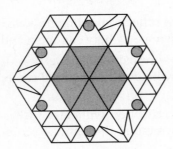

47. a. Since the prism is 4 cm high, it will take 4 layers.

b. The volume is the product of the first layer times 4, or $(4 \times 4) \times 4 = 16 \times 4 = 64$ cm³.

c. If we label the three dimensions x, y, z, then the volume V of the prism is $V = xyz$.

d. The cylinder is the same height as the prism, so it will also take 4 layers to fill.

e. If we estimate the base of the cylinder to have a radius of 2, then the estimated volume would be $(4\pi) \times 4 = 16\pi$.

f. If we label r as the radius of the cylinder and h as the height, then volume $V = (\pi r^2)h$.

g. The cylinder has a smaller volume than the prism with the same height and "diameter".

48. a. Pattern B

b. A and B

c. B and C. The center of rotation is the center of the rectangle or the point where the diagonals of the rectangle intersect. The angle of rotation is 180°.

d. We need the short side of the rectangle and one of the following; the radius, diameter, or circumference of the circle, or the other side of the rectangle not yet measured.

e. The first measurement determines h, while the second measurement will determine r.

f. $V = (\pi r^2)h$, so that $V = (36\pi)15 = 540\pi$ cm³

49. a. $V = \frac{1}{3}(3^2\pi)8 = 24\pi$ cm³

b. $V = \frac{1}{3}(\pi r^2)h$, that is, $\frac{1}{3} \times$ volume of the same dimension cyclinder

c. $V = \frac{1}{3} \times$ volume of the same dimension prism, or $A = \frac{1}{3}xyz$ where $x, y,$ and z are the side lengths of the prism.

d. $V = \frac{1}{3}(7^2 \times 12) = 196$ cm³

50. A possible basic design element is below left. There are vertical lines of symmetry through the center of each design element and through the center of each small triangle. There is no rotation symmetry.

51. A possible basic design element is below left. There are vertical lines of symmetry through the center of and between design elements; a horizontal line of symmetry through the center of the design; and rotational symmetry with an angle of rotation of 180° about the center of each design element and the point between design elements.

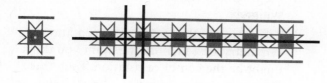

52. A possible basic design element is below left. There are vertical lines of symmetry through the centers of and between design elements, and a horizontal line of symmetry through the center of the design. There is rotation symmetry with an angle of rotation of 180° about the center of each design element and the point between design elements.

53. A possible basic design element is below left. There are vertical lines of symmetry through the middle and at both ends of each design element. There is no rotation symmetry.

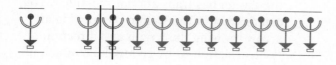

Extensions

54. **a.** Reflection symmetry: The lines of symmetry are diameters of the circle, passing through the vertices of the opposite hexagon, or the lines of symmetry pass through the midpoints of opposite sides of the hexagon. Rotation symmetry: 60° around the center of the circle.

b. 60°. The rotation symmetry ensures that the angles at the center are 60°. The fact that each triangle is isosceles (radii for equal sides) ensures that the other two angles are also 60°.

c. Possible answer:
- Draw any radius.
- Copy radius around circumference.

d. The symmetries in (a) are the same as for a kaleidoscope (which could have angles of rotation of 60° or 120°). The 60° rotation symmetry gives us the equilateral triangle. The reflections to make the hexagon are the same as the mirror reflections in a kaleidoscope.

55. **a.** Basic design element using only translations:

b. Smaller basic design element is:

This smaller basic design element can be used to make the design by using reflection and translation as follows:

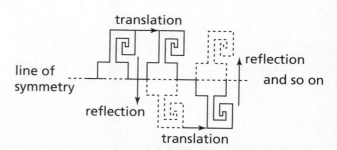

c. A glide reflection is a combination (or *composition*) of two transformations—a reflection and a translation. One difference is that, with a glide reflection, the resulting design does not have a line of symmetry.

56. Answers will vary. Possible answer:

57. a. Possible answers are given below. Note that that among the basic design elements the most basic is the rhombus and that for this case the basic design element always overlaps on an edge when you translate it to make the wallpaper design:

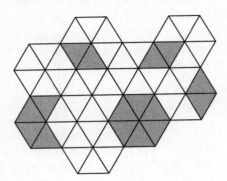

b. Possible answer using one of the rhombi as a basic element:

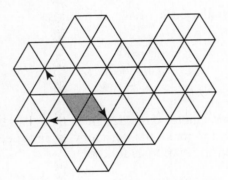

c. No; a triangle cannot be used as the basic element which can be translated. You must rotate or reflect the triangle at some time in order to get the upside down triangle in the design.

Possible Answers to Mathematical Reflections

1. a. There are several ways to determine that a design has reflection symmetry. For each method, you must first identify a line you think might be a line of symmetry. You can place a transparent reflection tool on the line. If the reflected image matches the image behind the tool, the design has reflection symmetry. If the design is on a sheet of paper, you can fold the design on the line. If the two halves match, the design has reflection symmetry. You can also trace the entire design or the part of the design on one side of the line and then flip your tracing over the line. If the tracing matches the original design, the design has reflection symmetry.

b. To determine that a design has rotation symmetry, first identify the point you think might be the center of rotation. Then trace the entire design, or just the basic design element, and rotate the tracing around the point. If the tracing matches the original design at some point before you finish a complete rotation, the design has rotational symmetry. You can find the angle of rotation by finding corresponding points on two consecutive basic design elements and then measuring the angle formed by line segments from the center of rotation to those points or by determining the total number of ways the design could be rotated to match with the original and dividing 360° by that number.

c. To determine that a design has translation symmetry, trace the design or the part you think might be a basic design element. If you can slide your tracing in a straight line so that it matches with the original design, the design has translational symmetry. You can describe a translation by drawing an arrow showing the length and direction of the translation or by giving the length and direction in words. In order to truly have translation symmetry, a figure needs to continue forever in some direction. You can slide the whole design a certain distance and it would look exactly the same as before it was moved.

2. a. To make a design with reflection symmetry, you can use a transparent reflection tool or tracing paper to make a design with reflection symmetry. First, you need to draw the basic design element and a line of reflection. To use the reflection tool, place the edge of the tool on the line of reflection. Look at the reflection of the basic design element, and trace the image on the other side of the line. To use tracing paper, trace the basic design element and the line of reflection on the tracing paper and then flip the tracing over the line, matching the line of reflection on your tracing with the line of reflection on the original. Press on key points on the tracing to make indentations on the final paper. Then remove the tracing paper and connect the indentations to make the final image. Instead of making indentations, you can retrace the figure through the back of the tracing paper. This will leave light pencil marks that you can retrace to show the image more clearly.

To test a design for reflection symmetry you can use a ruler to check that corresponding points are equal distances from the line of reflection. You can measure the angles that the line connecting a point and its image make with the line of symmetry to confirm that it is a right angle.

b. To make a design with rotational symmetry, draw the basic design element and a center of rotation. Trace the design element and the center of rotation, and then rotate the tracing through the desired angle about the center, using an angle ruler or a protractor to measure the angle from a key point on the original element to the corresponding point on the tracing. (The angle of rotation must be a factor of 360°.) Copy the rotated tracing onto the final paper. Repeat this process until you have made a complete rotation about the center of rotation. If you have a stamp of the basic design element, you can rotate the stamp through the desired angle of rotation and stamp the image.

To test a design for rotation symmetry you can use a ruler to check that corresponding points are equal distances from the center of rotation. You can use a protractor or angle rule to check that the measure of the angle formed by a point, the center of rotation and the point's image is the same for all points and their images.

c. To make a design with translation symmetry, you can use tracing paper and a ruler. First, draw a basic design element and trace it onto tracing paper. Then use the ruler to help you slide the tracing the desired direction and distance, and copy the tracing onto the final paper. Repeat this process several times. If you have a stamp of a basic design element, you can slide the stamp the desired direction and distance and stamp the image.

To test a design for translation symmetry you can use a ruler to check that all corresponding points are the same distance from each other. You can use a protractor or angle ruler to check that the angles formed by a horizontal line and the line running through corresponding points is the same for all points.

Mathematical and Problem-Solving Goals

- Use the properties of reflections, translations, and rotations to perform transformations

- Find lines of reflection, magnitudes and directions of translations, and centers and angles of rotation

- Examine and describe the symmetries of a design made from a figure and its image(s) under a symmetry transformation

- Give precise mathematical directions for performing reflections, rotations, and translations in terms of the transformation on points of the original figure

- Draw conclusions about a figure, such as measures of sides and angles, lengths of diagonals, or intersection points of diagonals, based on what symmetry or symmetries the figure has

- Learn to appreciate the power of transformational geometry to describe motions, patterns, designs and properties of shapes in the real world

Summary of Problems

Problem 2.1   Describing Line Reflections

Students observe properties that define a line reflection and would allow someone else to

perform it. Line reflections match points of a figure to points of an image figure. The original figure and its image form a design that has reflection symmetry.

Problem 2.2   Describing Rotations

Students observe properties that define a rotation and would allow someone else to perform it. They find that the rotation of a figure produces an image that together with the original will not produce a design with rotation symmetry unless the rotation is 180°. However, the rotation of a figure will produce a symmetric design if the angle of rotation is a factor, k, of 360 and the design has $\frac{360}{k}$ figures.

Problem 2.3   Describing Translations

Students observe properties that define a translation and would allow someone else to perform it. They find that if a translation of a figure is repeated infinitely, a strip design with translation symmetry is produced.

Problem 2.4   Using Symmetry to Think About Tessellations

Students examine tessellations to find basic elements of the design that can be used along with transformation of the element to reproduce the design. They also examine tessellation designs to describe the types of symmetry the design has.

	Suggested Pacing	Materials for Students	Materials for Teachers	ACE Assignments
All	$5\frac{1}{2}$ days	Student notebooks, graphing calculators tracing paper (or lightweight plain paper), grid paper, rulers, mirrors, transparent reflection tools, angle rulers or protractors (1 per group)	Blank transparency and transparency markers (optional), overhead graphing calculator (optional)	
2.1	$1\frac{1}{2}$ days	Labsheets 2.1A, 2.1B, 2ACE Exercises 1–5	Transparencies 2.1A, 2.1B	1–5, 16–18
2.2	$1\frac{1}{2}$ days	Labsheets 2.2A, 2.2B 2ACE Exercises 6, 7, 30, 31, 33	Transparencies 2.2A, 2.2B	6, 7, 19, 20, 29–33
2.3	1 day	Labsheets 2.3A, 2.3B 2ACE Exercises 8, 9	Transparencies 2.3A, 2.3B	8, 9, 21–23
2.4	1 day	Labsheets 2.4A, 2.4B 2ACE Exercises 10–15, 25, 26	Transparencies 2.4A, 2.4B	10–15, 24–28
MR	$\frac{1}{2}$ day			

2.1 Describing Line Reflections

Goals

- Use the properties of reflections to perform line reflections
- Find a line of reflection given a figure and its image
- Find the reflection image of a figure given a line of reflection
- Examine and describe the symmetries of a design made from a figure and its image(s) under a line reflection
- Give precise mathematical directions for performing reflections in terms of the effect of the transformation on the original figure

Launch 2.1

Ask students to keep their books closed. Draw the following figure on the board or the overhead (or use the transparency), and ask students to copy it.

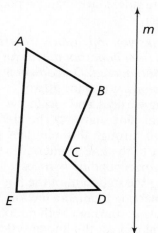

Now ask students to draw the reflection image of the polygon in the line, labeling matching points A', B', and so on.

Suggested Questions

- *How did you complete the line reflection?*
- *How can you show that it is a line reflection?*

- *What is the relationship between the figure you started with and the mirror image you drew?*

Listen to students' ideas and how they support them. If necessary, ask about the relationship between a vertex and its image. This exercise will help students begin to think about the concepts they will encounter throughout this investigation.

Drawing the reflection image of a figure is one kind of transformation. A *transformation* is a geometric operation that acts on the original figure and produces a copy of the figure in a new position. We call the copy the *image* of the original figure.

Read through the problem with the students so that they understand what is expected of them. Mention that they will be asked to give evidence to support their answers to each part of the problem during the summary.

Have students work on the problem in groups of three to four.

Explore 2.1

Circulate as groups work, asking questions to assess their understanding.

Suggested Questions

- *What patterns do you notice in the measurements you are making?*
- *How do the measurements you are making relate to the image you would get if you used a mirror to show the reflection image?*

If students are having trouble producing the reflection image for the figure in Question B, encourage them to draw on what they learned in Question A.

- *Look at what you discovered in Question A about the relationship between a figure and its image. How does a vertex on a polygon correspond to a vertex on the image of that polygon?* (Each vertex and its image are an equal, perpendicular distance from the line of reflection.)
- *How can you use this relationship to draw the image of the polygon in Question B?*

Once students have drawn the image, you may want to suggest that they use a transparent reflection tool, a mirror, or tracing paper to check their work.

Summarize 2.1

Ask students to share what they have learned from their work with line reflections.

Suggested Questions

- *When you connected vertices and images of those vertices using line segments, what did you observe about the collection of line segments?* (The line segments appear to be parallel.)

- *What did you observe about the line segments relative to the line of symmetry?* (The line segments appear to be perpendicular to the line of symmetry.)

- *What did you notice about the distance from the line of symmetry to a vertex and the corresponding distance from the line of symmetry to the image of that vertex?* (The distances are of equal length.)

- *What can you say about the point of intersection of the line of reflection and the line segment from a vertex to its image?* (The point of intersection is the midpoint of the segment.)

- *In mathematics when you talk about the distance from a point to a line, the distance is assumed to be the perpendicular distance to the line. You can see why this is important to specify, since you could all get different measures if you measured to anywhere on the line. In order for the measure to be meaningful, the distance from a point to the line of symmetry must be measured along a line perpendicular to the line of reflection.*

- *Summarize what these observations tell you about how to perform a line reflection using only a ruler and an angle ruler or a protractor.* (Draw a line segment from a vertex of the original figure perpendicular to the line of reflection, and measure its length. Extend the segment, and mark a point on it that is the same distance from the line of reflection but on the other side. This is the location of the image of the vertex. Do this for every vertex, and then connect the image vertices in the corresponding order to form the image polygon.)

- *In Investigation 1, you drew reflections in a line by folding paper or by using mirrors or transparent reflection tools. Why does the method you discovered in this problem give you the same results?* (When we folded paper or used a reflection tool to see the image of the original figure, every vertex was the same distance from the line of symmetry on the other side and in the same relative position. When we measure the distances, we make sure that each image point is the same distance from the line of reflection as the original point. If we fold the paper along the line between the point and its image, the line we make appears to be perpendicular to the line of reflection.)

Have several students show their reflected figure from Question B and the line of symmetry drawn for the figures in Question C.

- *Explain how to draw an image of a figure using only a ruler and an angle ruler or protractor.* (Draw lines from each vertex on the polygon perpendicular to the line of reflection and extending beyond it. Measure the length of the line segment from each vertex to the line of reflection and measure an equal distance from the line of reflection to the opposite side. Mark the new points and connect them.)

- *Question C asks you to reason in reverse: the reflection has been done, but the line of symmetry is not marked. Describe how to find the line of symmetry.* (Connect two corresponding vertices, and locate the midpoint of this line segment. The line of symmetry goes through this midpoint and is perpendicular to the line segment. If you use two pairs of corresponding vertices and repeat finding the midpoint of the line segment connecting them, the line of reflection must go through both midpoints. Therefore, you can get the line of reflection by drawing a line through the two midpoints.)

Question D asks students to complete a definition of a *line reflection*. Have two or three students share their answers. Each definition should capture the idea that point X' lies the same distance on the other side of the line of symmetry from point X on line segment XX', which is perpendicular to the line of symmetry.

Suggested Questions

- *If you draw a figure and a line of reflection on a piece of paper, every point on the paper has an image on the other side of the line of reflection. You can think of the piece of paper as a plane that goes on forever. When you do a line reflection, every point in the plane has an image point. You can picture a copy of the plane flipping in the line of reflection, carrying the figure with it. Are any points in the plane unmoved by a line reflection?* (The points on the line of reflection itself are unmoved— everything else is moved.)

Discuss Question E. Ask:

- *What is different about the figure and its image in Question E?* (The figure lies on the line so part of the image is on each side of the line.)

- *Is the reflection line a line of symmetry for the final design?* (Yes.)

- *This show us that points on one side of the reflection line have images on the opposite side of the reflection line. What happens to the points of the figure that are on the reflection line?* (They are fixed points. The image and original points are identical.)

2.1 Describing Line Reflections

Mathematical Goals

- Use the properties of reflections to perform line reflections
- Find a line of reflection given a figure and its image
- Find the reflection image of a figure given a line of reflection
- Examine and describe the symmetries of a design made from a figure and its image(s) under a line reflection
- Give precise mathematical directions for performing reflections in terms of the effect of the transformation on points of the original figure

Launch

Draw the figure on the overhead. Ask students to copy draw the reflection image of the figure in the line *m*.

- *How did you complete the line reflection?*
- *How can you show that it is a line reflection?*
- *What is the relationship between the figure you started with and the mirror image you drew?*

Drawing the reflection *image* of a figure is one kind of transformation. A *transformation* is a geometric operation that produces a copy of a figure in a new position.

Read through the problem with the students. Remind them that they should give arguments to support their answers.

Have students work on the problem in groups of four.

Materials
- Transparency 2.1A, 2.1B
- Mirrors or transparent reflection tool
- Rulers, angle rulers, or protractors

Explore

Circulate as groups work, asking questions;

- *What patterns do you notice in the measurements you are making?*
- *How do the measurements you are making relate to the image you would get if you used a mirror to show the reflection image?*

If students are having trouble with the reflection image for Question B, encourage them to use what they learned in Question A.

- *Look at what you discovered in Question A about the relationship between a figure and its image. How does a vertex on a polygon correspond to a vertex on the image of that polygon?*
- *How can you use this relationship to draw the image of the polygon in Question B?*

Materials
- Labsheet 2.1A, B

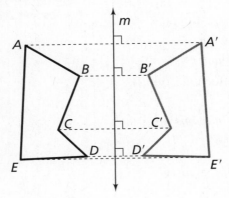
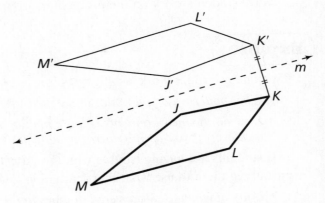
50 Kaleidoscopes, Hubcaps, and Mirrors

3. Yes. The design made by the pair of figures has reflection symmetry.

C.

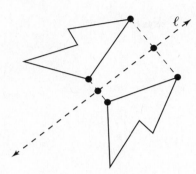

To find the line of symmetry, draw at least two lines connecting a vertex point and its image. Find the midpoint of each line and draw a line connecting these midpoints. This will be the reflection line.

D. ... point X' is the same distance from the line of reflection as point X is from the line of reflection, and XX' is perpendicular to the line of reflection.

E. 1. No, triangle DEF is scalene.

2.

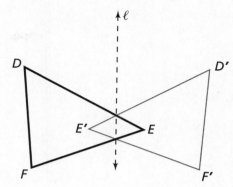

3. Yes. This design has reflection symmetry and the line of reflection is the reflection or mirror line for the design.

F. The fixed points are the points on the line of reflection. These points remain in the same place. All other points will have an image point on the opposite side of the line of reflection.

2.2 Describing Rotations

Goals

- Use the properties of rotations to find the rotation image of a figure

- Find the center and angle of rotation given a figure and its rotation image

- Find the rotation image of a figure given the center and the angle of rotation

- Examine and describe the symmetries of a design made from a figure and its rotation image

- Give precise mathematical directions for performing rotations in terms of the effect of the transformation on points of the original figure

- Draw conclusions about a figure, such as measures of sides and angles based on what symmetry or symmetries the figure has

- Learn to appreciate the power of transformational geometry to describe motions, patterns, designs and properties of shapes in the real world

Launch 2.2

Introduce the class to the topic of rotation transformation.

Suggested Questions

- *Name some things that you see in the world that rotate.* (Car tires, windmills, non-digital clock hands, the earth, CDs, merry-go-rounds, Ferris wheels, etc.)

- *How would you describe the way that they rotate? Is the rotation systematic?* (Yes. They rotate around a center point or axis.)

Remind students of their work in Investigation 1, perhaps displaying some of the hubcaps and kaleidoscope designs from that investigation.

- *In this problem, you will examine how to perform a rotation and how to find the image of an original figure under a rotation.*

You might demonstrate a rotation at the overhead by overlapping two transparencies of the compass star with the same point marked on each. Without explaining what you are doing, use the center point as the center of rotation by anchoring it with a pin and slowly rotating the top figure counterclockwise until it again coincides with the original figure. Stop at some point in the rotation and ask:

- *How could we measure how far I have rotated the figure?*

Let students offer their conjectures, and explain that they will learn about this idea as they work on the problem. Read through the problem with students, and have them explore it in pairs.

Explore 2.2

If students are having trouble understanding the relationship between a figure and its image after a rotation, encourage the use of tracing paper or blank transparencies to help them understand the motion involved. Students can draw the original figure on tracing paper and mark the center of the rotation. By anchoring the tracing paper at the center of the rotation with a pencil point and then rotating the paper, they can observe the movement of the image.

You might suggest that they imagine a point leaving a trail as it moves.

Suggested Questions

- *Suppose that as you rotate a copy of the figure, the vertices of the figure trace out their paths. What would the paths look like?* (A part of a circle, or an arc.)

Summarize 2.2

Call on students to share their observations from Question A. They should express the idea that the paths that points of the compass star would follow as they move to their images describe a quarter of a circle. They should also express the idea that a vertex and its image are the same distance from the center of rotation and that all the angles formed by a vertex, the center of rotation, and the image of that vertex in a particular rotation are 90°.

Have a student demonstrate how he or she performed the rotations in Question B. If others have found another way to think about the rotations, give them a chance to share their methods.

Here are two common methods:

Method 1: Draw a 60° angle moving counterclockwise with the line segment PR as one side. Mark off a line segment PR' which is the same length as PR. On that line segment, mark off PQ'. Lightly draw a line segment PS, and draw another 60° angle moving counterclockwise with PS as one side. Mark a segment PS'. Connect P, Q', R', and S' to get a rotated flag.

Method 2: Using P as the center and radii PR, PQ and PS, draw arcs from points R, Q and S. Measure 60° as before, using PR (or PQ or PS) as one side of the angle, and mark points R', Q', and S' on the arcs. Connect the points to make a rotated flag.

Have someone demonstrate how he or she rotated the image of the original polygon for the rectangle in Question C. Students should have observed that each image point travels along a circle to its final location.

Question D asks students to complete a definition of a rotation. Have two or three students share their answers. Each student should communicate the ideas that each vertex and its image are the same distance from the center of rotation, and that the angles formed by each vertex, the center of rotation, and the image of the vertex are all the same within a given rotation.

Suggested Question

- *If you draw a figure on paper, overlap it with a copy or tracing paper, and then rotate the copy, every point on the original paper has an image after the rotation. You can think of the piece of paper as a plane that goes on forever. When you do a rotation, every point in the plane has an image point. You can picture the copy of the plane rotating, carrying the figure with it. Are any points in the plane unmoved by a rotation?* (The point that is the center of rotation does not move—everything else is moved.)

2.2 Describing Rotations

Mathematical Goals

- Use the properties of rotations to find the rotation image of a figure
- Find the center and angle of rotation given a figure and its rotation image
- Find the rotation image of a figure given the center and the angle of rotation
- Examine and describe the symmetries of a design made from a figure and its rotation image
- Give precise mathematical directions for performing rotations in terms of the effect of the transformation on points of the original figure
- Draw conclusions about a figure, such as measures of sides and angles based on what symmetry or symmetries the figure has
- Learn to appreciate the power of transformational geometry to describe motions, patterns, designs and properties of shapes in the real world

Launch

Name some things that you see in the world that rotate.

- *How would you describe the way that they rotate? Is the rotation systematic?*

Demonstrate a rotation at the overhead by overlapping two transparencies of the compass star with the same point marked on each. Without explaining, use the center point as the center of rotation by anchoring it, and slowly rotate the top figure counterclockwise until it coincides with the original figure. Stop at some point and ask:

- *How could we measure how far I have rotated the figure?*

Have students work in pairs.

Materials
- Transparency 2.2A, 2.2B
- Mirrors or transparent reflecting tools
- Rulers, angle rulers, or protractors
- Tracing paper

Explore

Draw the original figure on tracing paper and mark the center of the rotation. Anchor the tracing paper at the center of the rotation with a pencil point and then rotate the paper, to observe the "movement" of the image. Imagine a point leaving a trail as it moves.

- *Suppose that as you rotate a copy of the figure, the vertices of the figure trace out their paths. What would the paths look like?*

Materials
- Labsheet 2.2A, B

Summarize

Have students share answers to Question A. The points move on a circular path around the center of the rotation. A vertex and its image point are the same distance from the center of the circle and the angles formed by a vertex, the center, and the image, are 90°.

Materials
- Student notebooks
- Labsheets 2ACE Exercises 6, 7, 30, 31, 33 (optional)

continued on next page

Call on students to demonstrate the rotations in Question B, the rotation of the polygon in Question C.

Put the stem for the definition of a rotation on the board and students give their answers for how a rotation is defined. Be sure that students see that you need to specify two pieces of information, the center for the rotation and the counterclockwise angle of rotation.

Ask students if there are any fixed points for the rotation; points that are their own image under the rotation.

Vocabulary
- rotations

ACE Assignment Guide for Problem 2.2

Core 6, 7, 19, 20
Other Extensions 29–33; unassigned choices from previous problems

Labsheets 2ACE Exercise 6, 2ACE Exercise 7 and 2ACE Exercises 30, and 2 ACE Exercises 31, 33 are provided if Exercises 6, 7, 30, 31, and 33 are assigned

Adapted For suggestions about adapting ACE exercises, see the CMP *Special Needs Handbook*. Assignment Guide for Problem 2.2

Answers to Problem 2.2

A. 1. 90 degrees

2. *A-G, G-E, E-C, C-A, H-F, F-D, D-B, B-H*

3. Arcs of circles; the radii of the circles depend on the distance between the point and the center of rotation.

4. The segments connecting them form a 90° angle. The path for each vertex forms an arc of a circle. The segments connecting the vertex or its image to the center of rotation are the radii for the circle.

B. 1. No. Line segments are of different lengths and there is no center around which to rotate.

2.

In order to draw a rotation, you need to use a protractor or angle ruler. For each point, moving in a counterclockwise direction measure off the angle of the rotation and the distance from the center and mark the new location. Each point will move in an arc of a circle the number of degrees in the rotation.

3. No. If you rotate, the image and the original will rotate and the design will be in a new location, and will not coincide with the original.

4. Only for 180° will the original and its image form a design with rotation symmetry.

5. Yes. Using 120° or 30° or any other proper factor of 360°, make the rotation images of the original for all multiples of the factor that are less than 360°. For example, the picture shows the original and its images for 120°. The final design has rotation symmetry.

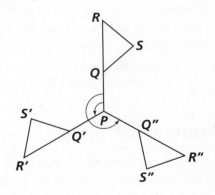

C. 1. Check students' drawings. Image should look similar to this:

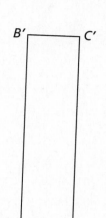

2.

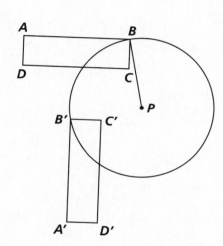

3. The images of vertex *A* and vertex *B* will each travel on a circle. The angle formed by *APA'* will equal the angle of rotation. For *B* and *B'* the angle *BPB'* will be the same as angle *APA'*. However, the radius of the circles on which the images of *A* and *B* are located are different.

4. Segments *AP* and *AP'* will be the same length. The line segments *BP* and *BP'* will be the same length, however, they will not necessarily equal the length of segments *AP* and *AP'*.

5. The angles are all equal to the angle of rotation, 90°.

D. A rotation of *d* degrees about a point *P* matches any point *X* with an image point *X'* so that segment *PX* is the same length as segment *PX'*, and angle *XPX'* has the same measure as the angle of rotation.

E. The center of rotation is the only point fixed by a rotation of the plane.

2.3 Describing Translations

Goals

- Use properties of translations to examine whether a given figure has translation symmetry

- Find the magnitude and direction of a translation given a figure and its translation image

- Find a translation image given the magnitude and direction or a vector (arrow) specifying the translation

- Examine and describe the translation symmetries of a design

- Give precise mathematical directions for performing translations in terms of the effect of the transformation on points of the original figure

Launch 2.3

Remind students of their work in Investigation 1, in which they explored translations and translation symmetry.

Suggested Questions

- *Look around the room. Do you see any patterns that show a translation?*

Explain that the goals of this problem are similar to those of the last, but with a different kind of motion: a translation, or slide. Pose the following question:

- *What is the relationship between a figure and its image under a translation? What measures are the same from the original to its image under translation?*

Read through the problem so that students know what is expected.

Each student should do his or her own work, but check and discuss observations with a partner.

Explore 2.3

If students are having difficulty, encourage them to trace the polygon on tracing paper and then slide the tracing so that they can see the translation in progress. Sometimes observing this actual motion is all a student needs to make sense of translations.

For Question B, students may need assistance to see that they can connect an original vertex with its image to determine the direction and the distance, or magnitude, of the translation. Extending this line and marking off the same distance will locate the image of the first image vertex under the same translation performed a second time.

Summarize 2.3

Suggested Questions

- *What patterns did you see when you connected each vertex with its image?* (The lines were parallel and the same length.)

- *Does this make sense?* (Yes; under a translation, each point should slide the same distance and direction.)

- *How did you slide the image figure to perform the second translation?*

In Question B, some students will be helped if you or a student shows how to use tracing paper to perform the translation. It helps to draw a dotted line to extend the line of translation so that the direction of the slide can be preserved during the demonstration. Then copy the figure and the translation arrow onto the tracing paper. Mark the beginning and end of the arrow clearly. Then slide the figure and mark the new image points by pressing hard on the tracing paper. Examine the results with the class. (Another way to carry out the translation is to imagine the figure on a grid. Then measure the angle the line of translation makes with the x-axis and use that measure and the length of the arrow to locate the vertex images.)

Question C asks students to complete a definition of a translation. Have two or three students share their answers. Each definition should communicate the idea that the line segments connecting each point and image are all parallel and the same length. Each point has moved the same distance and in the same direction.

Suggested Question

- *If you draw a figure on a piece of paper, you can think of the piece of paper as a plane that goes on forever. When you do a translation, every point in the plane has an image point. You can picture a copy of the plane translating, carrying the figure with it. Are any points in the plane unmoved by a translation?* (No.)

Describing Translations

Mathematical Goals

- Use properties of translations to examine whether a given figure has translation symmetry
- Find the magnitude and direction of a translation given a figure and its translation image
- Find a translation image given the magnitude and direction or a vector (arrow) specifying the translation
- Examine and describe the translation symmetries of a design
- Give precise mathematical directions for performing translations in terms of the effect of the transformation on points of the original figure

Launch

Remind students of their work in Investigation 1 on translations.

- *Look around the room. Do you see any patterns that show a translation?*

Explain that the goals of this problem are similar to those of the last, but with a different kind of motion: a translation, or slide. Ask:

- *What is the relationship between a figure and its image under a translation?*
- *What measures are the same from the original to its image under translation?*

Read through the problem so that students know what is expected. Each student should do his or her own work, but check and discuss observations with a partner.

Materials

- Transparency 2.3A, 2.3B
- Mirrors or transparent reflecting tools
- Rulers, angle rulers, or protractors

Explore

Encourage students to trace the polygon on tracing paper and then slide the tracing so that they can see the translation in progress. For Question B, students may need assistance to see that they can connect an original vertex with its image to determine the direction and the distance, or magnitude, of the translation. Extending this line and marking off the same distance will locate the image of the first image vertex under the same translation performed a second time.

Materials

- Labsheet 2.3A, B

Summarize

- *What patterns did you see when you connected each vertex with its image? Does this make sense?*
- *How did you slide the image figure to perform the second translation?*

Materials

- Student notebooks
- Labsheets 2ACE Exercises 8, 9 (optional)

continued on next page

For Question B, demonstrate with tracing paper how to carry out a translation. Also demonstrate how to superimpose a grid and measure the angle the translation makes with the x-axis and then measure the magnitude of the slide in this direction. Question C asks for a definition of a translation. Have students share their answers. Each definition needs to indicate that points in the plane are translated the same distance and in the same direction.

- *Are there any fixed points under a translation?*

ACE Assignment Guide for Problem 2.3

Differentiated Instruction
Solutions for All Learners

Core 8, 9, 21–23

Labsheet 2ACE 8, 9 is provided if Exercises 8 and 9 are assigned

Adapted For suggestions about adapting ACE exercises, see the CMP *Special Needs Handbook*. Assignment Guide for Problem 2.3

Answers to Problem 2.3

A. In a translation, the figure slides to a new location. Points move in straight lines and in the same direction. They also move the same distance in order to maintain the integrity of the shape. So $GG' = HH' = KK'$ etc. And GG' is parallel to HH' etc.

B. Check to make sure points are in the correct location and have moved the same distance from their original location.

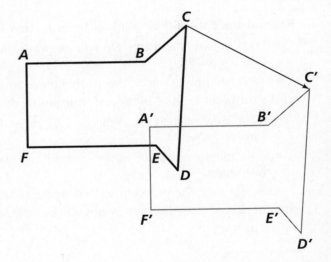

C. A translation matches points X and Y with images X' and Y' so that each new point is located a distance from the original points such that the distance and direction moved for all points is the same. i.e., $XX' = YY'$ and XX' is parallel to YY'.

D. All the points *move together* in a translation so no points are fixed.

Diagram 1

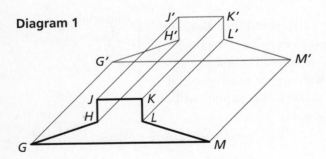

Diagram 2

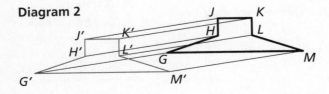

Goals

- Give precise mathematical directions for performing reflections, rotations, and translations

- Identify and use a basic design element and transformations on that element to reproduce a tessellation of the plane

- Learn to appreciate the power of transformational geometry to describe motions, patterns, designs and properties of shapes in the real world

Launch 2.4

Look at the example of a tessellation given in the SE. Have the students examine the *tessellation* to identify a part of the design from which the entire design can be made. This is called a *basic design element.*

If the tessellation has translation symmetry, after you draw the original design element, you can slide your pen to a new position and repeat your drawing. Then you move the same distance and direction to a new position, repeat the drawing, and keep going in the same way. The question is whether, in principle, you can move and redraw the basic element through translation to cover the entire tessellation of the plane. You may want to illustrate this process with the idea of making a stamp of a basic design element and using that stamp repeatedly to re-draw a pattern.

Note that with a different basic element for a tessellation, you may need to perform other transformations in addition to translations to fill the entire design.

Use the question in the SE to get students thinking about the tessellation.

Suggested Questions

- *What part of the tessellation do you think can be a basic pattern for redrawing the tessellation using translation?* (The shaded square with one of the small white squares,

Some may try to use a shaded square with all four small squares. The problem with this is that you get overlap of parts of the design.)

Here are other possible basic design elements and translation arrows to cover the tessellation:

- *What direction would you give to carry out the translation?* (We can reproduce the tessellation by sliding the basic design element at a horizontal, vertical or 45° angle from horizontal.)

- *Would your directions be precise enough for someone to remake this pattern exactly?* (You would need a distance to translate as well as a direction.)

- *Does this design have rotation symmetry?* (90° rotation around the center of any square in the design.) *Reflection symmetry?* (No.)

Have the students work on these problems individually and then compare their answers in groups of three or four.

Explore 2.4

Some students may find these problems easier with tracing paper or transparencies. As they work, you may want to remind students that tessellations go on forever in every direction. What we see is only a part of the design.

If students in a group quickly find a basic design element, challenge them to find another possibility. There are several.

Summarize 2.4

For Question A, encourage students to share the various ways that they identified the basic design element for the tessellation and specified the translation for each basic design element. It is extremely powerful for them to see that there are many correct ways to specify design elements and translations for the tessellation.

Call on a group to show a basic design element at the overhead.

Suggested Questions

- *Do you all agree that this basic design element can be used to reproduce the design? Why or why not?*

- *Give a set of precise directions for a translation of the design element that will cover the tessellation.*

Once the class accepts or corrects the design element and specifies a translation that will work, ask:

- *Let's collect every possible way you can think of to specify basic elements and translations that will remake this tessellation.*

Collect as many examples as the class offers in a few minutes.

- *Do you think these are the only directions we could give that would help someone remake this tessellation?* (There are many.)

For Question B, have groups discuss their work on each of the two designs.

- *How are the two designs different?* (The pattern of light and dark triangle is different.)

- *Which was harder to reproduce with transformations and why?* (Most students find Tevin's design harder. The obvious slide is the one that works for Rosslyn, but it produces her design, not Tevin's.)

- *Can you find a translation of the basic element given for Tevin's design that will reproduce the design? Why or why not?* (You need a rotation to get the black triangle in the position of the white triangle, followed by a translation, to see that the design can be covered.)

- *Does the tessellation have translation symmetry with a different basic element?* (Yes. If you choose a parallelogram made of 2 dark and 2 white triangles, you can translate this parallelogram to reproduce the design. Thus, a translation twice the length of the base of the basic design element will create an image that is identical to the original.)

Mathematical Goals

- Give precise mathematical directions for performing reflections, rotations, and translations
- Identify and use a basic design element and transformations on that element to reproduce a tessellation of the plane
- Learn to appreciate the power of transformational geometry to describe motions, patterns, designs and properties of shapes in the real world

Launch

Use the question in the SE to get students thinking about the tessellation.

- *What part of the tessellation do you think can be a basic pattern for redrawing the tessellation using translation?*
- *What direction would you give to carry out the translation? Would your directions be precise enough for someone to remake this pattern exactly?*
- *Does this design have rotation symmetry? Reflection symmetry?*

Have the students work on these problems individually and then compare their answers in groups of three or four.

Materials
- Transparency 2.4A, 2.4B
- Mirrors or transparent reflecting tools
- Rulers, angle rulers, or protractors

Explore

Some students may find these problems easier with tracing paper or transparencies. As they work, you may want to remind students that tessellations go on forever in every direction. What we see is only a part of the design.

If students in a group quickly find a basic design element, challenge them to find another possibility. There are several.

Materials
- Labsheet 2.4A, 2.4B

Summarize

Call on a group to show a basic design element at the overhead. Ask:

- *Do you all agree that this basic design element can be used to reproduce the design? Why or why not?*
- *Give a set of precise directions for a translation of the design element that will cover the tessellation.*
- *Let's collect every way you can think of to specify basic elements and translations that will remake this tessellation.*
- *Question B: How are the two designs different?*
- *Which was harder to reproduce with transformations and why?*
- *Can you find a translation of the basic element given for Tevin's design that will reproduce the design? Why or why not?*
- *Does the tessellation have translation symmetry with a different basic element?*

Materials
- Student notebooks
- Labsheets 2ACE Exercises 10, 11–15 (optional)

Vocabulary
- tessellation
- basic design element

ACE Assignment Guide for Problem 2.4

Core 10–15
Other *Connections* 24–28; unassigned choices from previous problems

Labsheets 2ACE Exercise 10, 2ACE Exercise 11, 2ACE Exercise 25 and 2ACE Exercise 26 are provided if Exercises 10, 11, 25 or 26 are assigned.

Adapted For suggestions about adapting Exercises 10–13, 2ACE Exercises 14–15, and other ACE exercises, see the CMP *Special Needs Handbook*.

Connecting to Prior Units 24–26: *Stretching and Shrinking;* 28: *Filling and Wrapping*

Answers to Problem 2.4

A. 1. Tessellation 2:

(There are other basic design elements that will work see below for examples.)

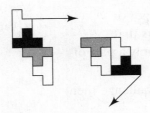

2. By sliding this basic design element horizontally and vertically, we can reproduce the tessellation. The distance is indicated by the length of the arrow joining corresponding points.

3. The design has neither because of the shading.

B. 1. Because of the shading, this parallelogram has no symmetries. Without the shading, it would have a 180° rotational symmetry, but no reflection symmetry.

2. For Rosslyn's design, a translation horizontally the length of the base would fill the gap and complete the pattern.

For Tevin's design, a rotation of 180° around the midpoint of the diagonal to get the blue triangle in the position of the gold triangle followed by a translation horizontally the length of the base that would fill the gap and complete the pattern. Other answers include: a translation followed by a rotation or a single rotation around the midpoint of the a side of the light colored triangle.

3. Both have translation symmetry. The slide that Rosslyn used works for her figure. For Tevin's design, a translation horizontally that is twice the length of the base of the rhombus translates the whole figure on top of itself.

4. Neither completed design has reflection symmetry. Tevin's design can be rotated 180° around the intersection of the diagonals of either a blue or gold parallelogram.

Investigation 2

ACE
Assignment Choices

Differentiated Instruction
Solutions for All Learners

Problem 2.1

Core 1–5, 16
Other *Connections* 17, 18; unassigned choices from previous problems

Problem 2.2

Core 6, 7, 19, 20
Other *Extensions* 29–33; unassigned choices from previous problems

Problem 2.3

Core 8, 9, 21–23

Problem 2.4

Core 10–15
Other *Connections* 24–28; unassigned choices from previous problems

Adapted For suggestions about adapting Exercises 10–13 and other ACE exercises, see the CMP *Special Needs Handbook*.
Connecting to Prior Units 18, 21: *Shapes and Designs;* 24–26: *Stretching and Shrinking;* 28: *Filling and Wrapping*

Applications

1. See illustration below. A' is the same distance from the line of symmetry as A. AA' is perpendicular to the line of symmetry. Triangle $A'B'C'$ is the image of triangle ABC. Each point on triangle ABC is matched to an image point on the other side of the line of reflection. Each image point lies on a line passing though the original point that is perpendicular to the line of reflection. The distance from the image point to the line of reflection is equal to the distance from the original point to the line of reflection.

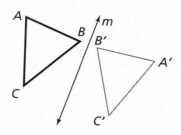

2. a.

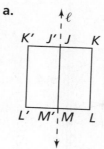

b. Yes the final drawing has reflection symmetry. The part of the final drawing on one side of the line of reflection corresponds exactly to the part of the drawing on the other side.

3. a.

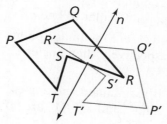

b. Yes the final drawing has reflection symmetry. The part of the final drawing on one side of the line of reflection corresponds exactly to the part of the drawing on the other side.

4. a. To find the line of reflection, place a line so that each point of figure $ABCD$ and its image figure $A'B'C'D'$ are equal distances on opposite sides of the line of reflection.

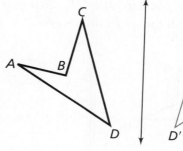

b. Each point of figure $ABCD$ and its image figure $A'B'C'D'$ are equal distances away from the line of reflection and the segment joining each point in figure $ABCD$ to its image point in $A'B'C'D'$ is perpendicular to the line of reflection.

5. a and b.

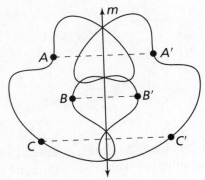

Each point and its image are equal distances on opposite sides of the line of reflection. The lines are parallel to each other and perpendicular to line m.

6. a. If X', Y' and Z' are the image points of X, Y, and Z respectively, then angles $\angle XZX'$ and $\angle YZY'$ are 90°.

b. The shape is maintained and angles $\angle XRX'$, $\angle ZRZ'$, and $\angle YRY'$ are 90°.

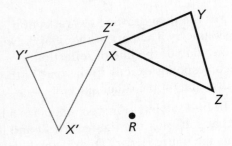

7. a. Straight angles through K are formed between the points and their respective images. $\overline{JK} = \overline{J'K}$, etc., and J, J' are points on a circle with center K, radius $\overline{JK}$.

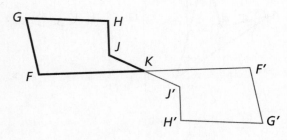

b. Straight angles through R are formed between the points and their respective images. $JR = J'R$, and J, J' are points on a circle with center R, radius JR.

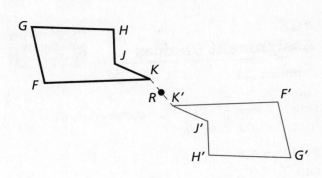

8. The shape slides down to its new location in the direction and distance of the arrow. $PP' = QQ' = RR'$ and line PP' is parallel to line QQ', etc.

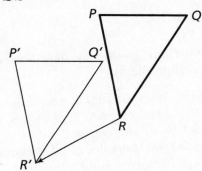

9. a.

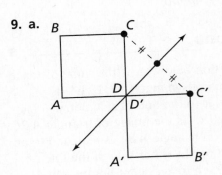

b.

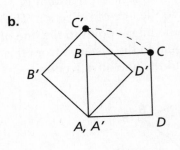

c.

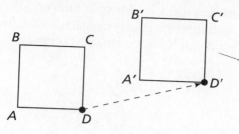

10. The transformation is a translation with the length and direction indicated by the arrow.

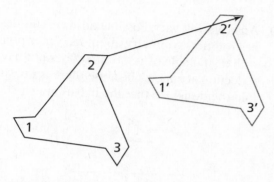

11. The transformation is a reflection in the line shown below.

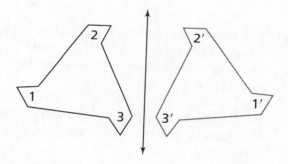

12. The transformation is a 180° rotation about the point shown.

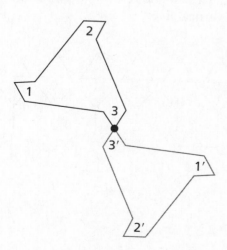

13. The transformation is a translation with the length and direction indicated by the arrow.

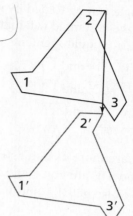

14. a.

b. The tessellation has translation symmetry.

c. We could move the design horizontally (1.5 cm), vertically (2.5 cm) and at 60° and 120° (1.5 cm) angles. Finally, the design does not have rotational symmetry.

15. a. Basic design element:

b. The tessellation has translation symmetry.

c. We could move the design horizontally (1 cm), vertically (1 cm) or at 60° and 120° angles (1.25 cm). There are two lines of symmetry: at 60° and 120° angles, running through the centers of the stars. The tessellation has 180° rotational symmetry around the center of each star and around the center of the small square.

Connections

16. The lines in the figure are lines of symmetry, so the rectangle can be folded over these lines and parts of the rectangle will match up. Thus the following are equal segments:

$\overline{SW}$ and $\overline{TW}$, $\overline{SW}$ and $\overline{VY}$,

$\overline{TW}$ and $\overline{UY}$, $\overline{UY}$ and $\overline{VY}$,

$\overline{SZ}$ and $\overline{TX}$, $\overline{ZV}$ and $\overline{XU}$,

$\overline{SZ}$ and $\overline{ZV}$, $\overline{TX}$ and $\overline{XU}$

Note: There are more examples. For instance since $\overline{WT}$ and $\overline{SW}$ are equal and $\overline{SW}$ and $\overline{VY}$ are equal, we also get $\overline{WT}$ and $\overline{VY}$ are equal.

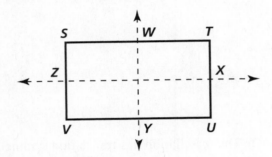

17. Possible answer: A square has four lines of symmetry: The vertical line through the center, the horizontal line through the center and the two diagonals. A square also has rotational symmetry about its center point with 90° angles of rotation.

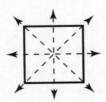

18. 144°; Explanations will vary. Students may triangulate the 10-sided polygon and will notice that there are 8 triangles each with 180°. Thus $(8 \times 180°) \div 10 = 144°$ in each angle of the 10-sided polygon.

19. Answers will vary. Possible answer: This design has reflection symmetry in the line shown, but it has no rotation symmetry.

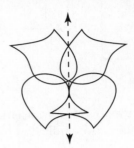

20. Answers will vary. Possible answer: This design has rotation symmetry about its center point with a 90° angle of rotation. It does not have reflection symmetry because there is no way to fold the design so that the halves match.

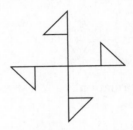

21. No; The angle measure of the interior angle of a regular hexagon is 120° and the angle measure of an interior angle of a regular pentagon is 108°. Since $120° + 120° + 108 = 348° \neq 360°$, you can't put together a regular pentagon and 2 regular hexagons around a vertex to form a tessellation.

22. Answers will vary. Possible answer: The design below has translation symmetry as indicated by the arrow and reflection symmetry over the vertical line:

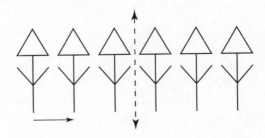

23. Answers will vary. Possible answer: The design below has translation symmetry as indicated by the arrow, but it has no reflection symmetry because there is no way to fold the design so that the halves match.

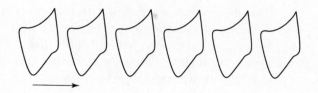

24. a.

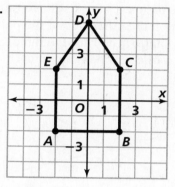

b. 22 sq. units

c.

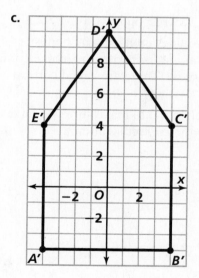

The two figures are similar. Each side is twice the length of the original side and all angles remain equal.

d. 88 sq. units (4 times as large as the original)

e. Answers will vary. Any rule of the form (ax, ay) where $0 < a < 1$.

25. a. Answers will vary. Possible answer: (all subsequent answers in this problem are based on this one.)

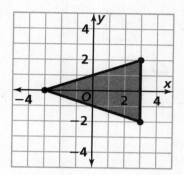

b.

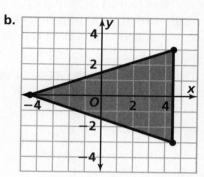

This figure is similar to the original with a scale factor of 1.5.

c.

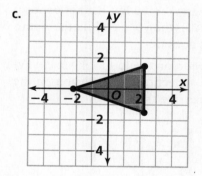

This figure is similar to the original with a scale factor of 0.75.

d. Yes, the two images are similar. The scale factor from the image in c to the image in b is $\frac{4}{3} \cdot \frac{3}{2} = 2$. This is true regardless of the original figure.

26. a. The scale factor is 2.

b.

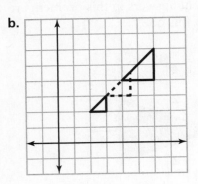

c. The new triangle is the same shape as the original and has moved right and up from the original position, as in translations. But the size has changed, which is NOT true for a translation.

27. D. Parallelograms have a center of rotation where the diagonals meet.

28. a. V = area of base × height, so $V = (\frac{1}{2} \times 2 \times 3) \times 10 = 30$ cm^3

b. $V = \frac{1}{3}$ × area of prism with same dimensions, so $V = 10$ cm^3

Extensions

29. a. The polygon on the left has reflection symmetry in the y-axis, while the figure on the right does not.

b. The polygon on the left looks unchanged after the reflection. The polygon on the right looks like this:

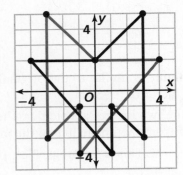

c. The image of the symmetric figure coincides with the original figure; the image of the non-symmetric figure does not.

d. If a figure with reflection symmetry in the y-axis is reflected in that axis, the image will coincide with the original figure. If a figure that does not have reflection symmetry in the y-axis is reflected in that axis, the image will not coincide with the original figure. This means that the design with reflection symmetry looks the same after the reflection. The design without reflection symmetry does not look the same, but the design and its image together form a symmetric design.

30. a. M still sits on line ℓ and K still sits on line n, but on the other side of the point of rotation, point B. They are the same distance from B as when they started.

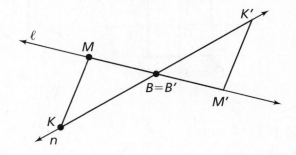

b. $\angle M'B'K'$ corresponds with $\angle MBK$.

c. When two lines intersect, the opposite angles that are formed in the intersection are congruent. These are called vertical angles.

31. a. Check reflection to make sure you have the points in the correct location.

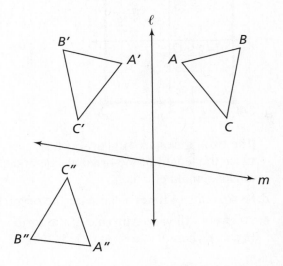

b. Yes. You could rotate the figure around the

point of intersection. That would get you the same result as two reflections.

c. In general, a reflection of a figure over two intersecting lines is equivalent to a single rotation about the point of intersection and an angle of rotation that is twice the measure of the angle between the lines.

32. a. The image of the polygon on the left has rotational symmetry about the origin.

b. The polygon on the left (the octagon) looks unchanged after the rotation. The image of the polygon on the right (the triangle) looks like this after the rotation:

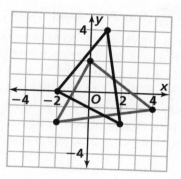

c. The rotation image of the symmetric figure coincides with the original figure. The rotation image of the non-symmetric figure does not.

33. a.

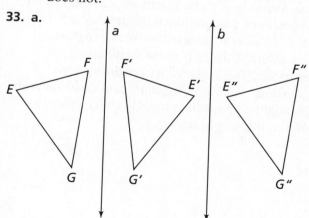

b. There is a single transformation that moves *EFG* to its final location.
When you reflect the second time, it flips the shape back to its original orientation. You could have just translated the shape to its final location.

c. Two reflections over parallel lines equals one translation

Possible Answers to Mathematical Reflections

1. a. A line through a point and its image will be perpendicular to the line of reflection. A point and its image are equal distances from the line of reflection.

b. You can connect a point and its image with a line segment. The line of reflection will be perpendicular to this line and will cut it in half (the line of reflection will be the perpendicular bisector).

2. a. A point and its image will be equal distances from the center of rotation. The center of rotation is on the perpendicular bisector of the line joining a point and its image.

b. You can draw a line segment from the center of rotation to a point, *A*, and another line segment from the center to the image *A'*. The angle between these two line segments is the angle of rotation. To find the image of a point *B*, draw the line segment connecting *B* to the center, then another line segment of the same length using the angle of rotation. *B'* will be at the end of this segment.

3. a. The image of each point will be a fixed distance from the point, measured in a fixed direction.

b. By drawing a line segment between a point *A* and its image *A'*, you can find the distance and direction of the translation. You can then make a line parallel to this segment, starting at *B*, and on this line you can copy the same distance as *AA'* to find the image *B'*.

4. A basic design element is a part of the design, which can be translated, reflected or rotated to make the entire tessellation. Possible explanation: In problem 2.4, the parallelogram consisting of a shaded and an unshaded triangle is the basic design element for Rosalyn's tessellation since it can be translated to make the entire tessellation.

Mathematical and Problem-Solving Goals

- Develop shape sense that helps in recognizing when two polygons are congruent

- Connect the notions of symmetry transformations to an informal strategy for checking to see whether given figures are congruent

- Develop ability to match corresponding parts of congruent figures and to express those correspondences in standard notation

- Discover minimal conditions about corresponding sides and angles of triangles from which one can infer congruence of the two figures—SAS, ASA, SSS

- Use reasoning about symmetry transformations and congruence conditions for triangles, to deduce further information about given figures

Mathematics Background

For background on congruent figures, see page 8.

Summary of Problems

Problem 3.1 Relating Symmetry and Congruence

This problem relies on students' informal sense of *same shape and size* to imagine the ways that two congruent polygons would be matched if corresponding congruent parts are *face-to-face*. Standard notation for expressing congruence of segments and angles (e.g. $\overline{AB} \cong \overline{CD}$ and $\angle ABC \cong \angle DEF$) is introduced, and students are asked to think about the symmetry transformations required to compare congruent figures.

Problem 3.2 Congruent Triangles

This problem develops students' ability to recognize congruent triangles within diagrams that contain several adjacent and overlapping figures. They are asked to match corresponding parts of congruent triangles and to use what they know about symmetry of rectangles and properties of parallel lines and transversals to reason informally in support of their conjectures about congruent figures.

Problem 3.3 The Matching Game

This problem asks students to play a matching game that requires constructing triangles congruent to given figures and, by analyzing strategies that help one to win that matching game, to discover minimal sets of information that guarantee congruence of two triangles. These are the familiar Side-Angle-Side and Angle-Side-Angle conditions.

Problem 3.4 Polystrip Triangles and Quadrilaterals

This problem connects student ideas about properties that give triangles their shapes (from the *Shapes and Designs* unit of year one) to the problem of using minimal information about triangle sides to decide whether triangles are congruent. This leads to the familiar Side-Side-Side congruence condition. One question about drawing congruent quadrilaterals highlights the special property of triangles that makes them rigid figures.

	Suggested Pacing	Materials for Students	Materials for Teachers	ACE Assignments
All	$5\frac{1}{2}$ days	Student notebooks, graphing calculators, tracing paper (or lightweight plain paper), grid paper, rulers, mirrors, transparent reflection tools, angle rulers or protractors (1 per group)	Blank transparency and transparency markers (optional), overhead graphing calculator (optional), chart paper	
3.1	1 day	Labsheets 3.1, 3ACE 1–4	Transparencies 3.1A, 3.1B	1–4, 17, 18
3.2	1 day	Labsheet 3.2	Transparency 3.2	5, 6, 19–23
3.3	2 days	Labsheet 3.3	Transparencies 3.3A, 3.3B	7–10, 27–29
3.4	1 day	Labsheet 3.4, polystrips	Transparency 3.4	11–16, 24–26
MR	$\frac{1}{2}$ day			

Goals

- Develop shape sense that helps in recognizing when two polygons are congruent

- Connect the notions of symmetry transformations to an informal strategy for checking to see whether given figures are congruent

- Develop ability to match corresponding parts of congruent figures and to express those correspondences in standard notation

- Use symmetry transformations to reason about congruence of polygons

Launch 3.1

You might project the display of turtle sketches and ask students: "Which of these turtles seems different from the others?" If a student suggests that "The middle one is bigger", ask whether it would be possible to make a case for some other figure being the odd turtle out.

You might then introduce the term *congruence* by noting that four of the five turtles are the same size and shape, and that mathematicians say one figure "is congruent to" another.

You might transition to the Getting Ready question by asking students how they would convince themselves that the four smaller turtles really are congruent. They will probably suggest some tracing or cut-out-and-move strategy. You might have a copy of one small turtle prepared to be moved around on the picture of five turtles. Then ask a student to give you directions on how to move that copy from its position on top of one turtle to a position on top of one of the others. Ask the student to use the symmetry transformation ideas from Investigation 2.

Focus student attention on the goal of the exploration by asking them to look at the two given quadrilaterals and to decide how, if *ABCD* could be maneuvered so that it would lie exactly on top of *PQRS*, the *corresponding* vertices would match up. Without accepting any answers, set the students to work on the questions.

Arrange students in pairs to work the problem.

Explore 3.1

Keep an eye out to see that students are using the suggested notation by asking them to show their recorded answers and to explain how the various notations would be read.

If students struggle, suggest that they draw a copy on tracing paper so that they can experiment to fit the copy over another figure. The moves should be described in transformation language.

Summarize 3.1

Have students report their answers to questions A–C using the phrases "corresponds to" and "is congruent to."

It is conventional to list these kinds of correspondence of congruent parts of figures so that not only are congruent segments matched correctly, but the segment endpoints are listed so that corresponding endpoints match. For example, you would not generally say that segment $\overline{AB}$ is congruent to segment $\overline{SR}$, even though the two segments are congruent. You might also choose not to be too fussy about notation at this time. If some students write that $\overline{AB} \cong \overline{SR}$, and others propose that $\overline{AB} \cong \overline{RS}$, you might ask if these are both correct. This gets students focusing on what congruent means (equal length in segments). We could certainly transform $\overline{AB}$ to fit $\overline{RS}$ or $\overline{SR}$. When we apply that same transformation to $ABCD$, we would want to match $\overline{AB}$ with $\overline{RS}$.

It might be good to press students to explain how they decided which vertices, segments, and angles correspond. In all likelihood, their answers will probably include some comment about measuring segments and angles or imagining motion of one figure onto the other. Note that it is possible to match some parts of the two figures in a way that does not match all the other points correctly. For example, matching A with Q and D with R will match two segments correctly. However, the other parts of the figures will not be matched "face to face."

3.1 Relating Symmetry and Congruence

Mathematical Goals

- Develop shape sense that helps in recognizing when two polygons are congruent
- Connect the notions of symmetry transformations to an informal strategy for checking to see whether given figures are congruent
- Develop ability to match corresponding parts of congruent figures and to express those correspondences in standard notation
- Use symmetry transformations to reason about congruence of polygons

Launch

Introduce the term *congruence* by noting that four of the five turtles are really the same size and shape, the four "are congruent to" each other.

Use the Getting Ready. Ask students how they would convince themselves or someone else that the four smaller turtles really are congruent.

Look at the two given quadrilaterals and to decide how, if *ABCD* could be maneuvered so that it would lie exactly on top of *PQRS*, the *corresponding* vertices would match up. Without accepting any answers from the whole class, set the students to work on the questions A–D addressing precisely the "corresponding parts" questions.

Arrange students in pairs to work on the problem.

Materials
- Transparency paper and tracing paper
- Transparency 3.1A, 3.1B
- Mirrors or transparent reflecting tools
- Rulers, angle rulers, or protractors

Explore

Check to see that they are using the suggested notation by asking students to show their recorded answers and to explain how the various notations would be *read*.

If students struggle, suggest that they draw a copy on tracing paper or transparent paper and experiment with moving a figure systematically to fit over another figure. The *moves* should be described in transformation language.

Materials
- Labsheet 3.1

Summarize

Have students report their answers to Questions A–C using phrasing with the phrases *corresponds to* and *is congruent to*. For example, Vertex *A* *corresponds to* vertex *R*, segment $\overline{AB}$ is congruent to segment $\overline{RS}$.

It is conventional to list these kinds of correspondence of congruent parts of figures so that not only are congruent segments matched correctly, but the segment endpoints are listed so that corresponding endpoints match.

Ask students to explain how they decided which vertices, segments, and angles correspond.

Materials
- Student notebooks
- Labsheet 3ACE1–4 (optional)

Vocabulary
- congruent
- congruence
- corresponds

Core 1–4, 17, 18

Other Labsheet 3ACE Exercises 1–4 is provided if Exercises 1–4 are assigned

Adapted For suggestions about adapting Exercises 1–4 and other ACE exercises, see the CMP *Special Needs Handbook*.

Connecting to Prior Units 17, 18 *Covering and Surrounding*

Answers to Problem 3.1

A. The only correspondence of vertices that will exactly match the two quadrilaterals gives:
$A \rightarrow R, B \rightarrow S, C \rightarrow P,$ and $D \rightarrow Q.$

B. The corresponding sides in the two figures will be: $\overline{AB} \cong \overline{RS}, \overline{BC} \cong \overline{SP}, \overline{CD} \cong \overline{PQ},$ and $\overline{DA} \cong \overline{QR}$

C. The corresponding angles in the two figures will be:
$\angle A \cong \angle R, \angle B \cong \angle S,$
$\angle C \cong \angle P,$ and $\angle D \cong \angle Q.$

D. Motions that would map one figure onto the other:

1. There is a single rotation that will map *ABCD* onto *RSPQ* (with vertices in that order). However, it is not at all obvious what either the center or the angle of that rotation will be. The center has to be equidistant from *C* and *P* and equidistant from *D* and *Q*. You can discover the center by drawing the perpendicular bisectors of segments $\overline{CP}$ and $\overline{DQ}$ and noting where they intersect (points equidistant from *C* and *P* and equidistant from *D* and *Q*).

2. There are several possible answers. You could translate *C* to *P* and then rotate the figure about *P* as a center until segment $\overline{CD}$ lies on top of $\overline{PQ}$. You could translate any vertex to its corresponding vertex and rotate until the rest of the figure matches. (Note that this works because the orientation of the two figures is the same. If one were reflected, you would need a reflection to undo the original reflection and then proceed to match vertices.)
You can also rotate *ABCD* about *A* until $\overline{AB}$ is parallel to $\overline{RS}$. Then translate the figure in the direction $\overline{AR}$ until *A* matches *R*.

E. *ABCD* and *RSPQ*. Note that *PQRS* is a labeling of the vertices independent of its connection to *ABCD*. The labeling *RSPQ* matches the vertices with the corresponding vertex of *ABCD*.

Congruent Triangles

Goals

- Connect the notions of symmetry transformations to an informal strategy for checking to see whether given figures are congruent

- Develop ability to match corresponding parts of congruent figures and to express those correspondences in standard notation

- Use reasoning about symmetry transformations and properties of figures with embedded triangles to deduce further information about given figures

Launch 3.2

You might begin focusing students' attention on the key figure to be studied in this problem by asking them why the rectangles in the bridge picture all seem to be criss-crossed by diagonals to produce four triangles. If they recall their work with polystrips in *Shapes and Designs*, they will remember the rigidity of triangles and the non-rigidity of quadrilaterals and point out that triangularization by introducing such braces will make a rectangular outer shape rigid and strong.

In case the students don't recall anything relevant, you might have some polystrip figures prepared to demonstrate the basic principle. Your figures might be built to look like this:

 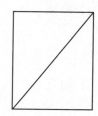 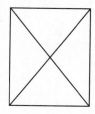

You might continue the launch of the problem by posing question A of Problem 3.2 and giving students a few minutes to come up with a conjecture about the number of triangles that can be seen in the given figure. There are eight.

To set students off on the rest of the problem, you might suggest something like this, "The task in this problem is to find as many pairs of congruent triangles as you can and to find ways to justify your idea about each such pair." You might give them a start by asking for one pair that they think is congruent, showing how to write that claim in correct notation, and guiding them through an argument of why the pair is congruent.

For example, they might naturally believe that $\triangle PTS \cong \triangle QTR$ (make sure that point T is in position indicating that it corresponds to itself). If you ask them how they could flip turn or slide one triangle onto the other to check, the reasoning supporting their view might be something like this:

"The rectangle is symmetric about a vertical line through its center, so that a reflection transformation would flip P to Q, S to R, and T to itself. That means that $\triangle PTS$ will can be transformed to fit exactly onto $\triangle QTR$, so the triangles are congruent."

At this point in the unit we don't expect any more rigorous argument. The familiar criteria like SAS, ASA, and SSS come later in the investigation. In fact, the above argument is logically equivalent to a traditional proof based on the SSS theorem.

Arrange students in pairs or groups of three or four to work on the problem.

Explore 3.2

Let the students proceed to complete their list of proposed congruent triangle pairs, watching to see that they record their ideas with correct notation and that, after using their eyes to spot potential congruent triangles, they are developing transformation arguments to explain why the proposed triangles in each pair could be matched *face to face*.

Note that it is possible to propose $\triangle PTQ \cong \triangle RTS$. This congruence would be checked by a half-turn rotation about point T, since the statement identifies P and R as corresponding vertices.

Summarize 3.2

It might be useful to generate a class list of congruent triangle pairs. Again, be careful to check the correspondences of vertices indicated by the proposed notation. For example, a claim like $\triangle PQT \cong \triangle STR$ has not followed the standard notational convention. However, both statements $\triangle PQT \cong \triangle STR$ and $\triangle PQT \cong \triangle RST$ are logically congruent, the latter is using the correct notation which matches up the vertices.

To help students justify their claims with transformation arguments, it might be helpful to have a large copy of the overall figure and of the three basic triangle parts of the figure ($\triangle PTQ$, $\triangle PTS$, and $\triangle PQS$ are the three different shapes in the figure). Another option would be to have two copies of an overhead transparency of the same figure. By moving the top copy, the correspondence of vertices after transformation will be evident.

It will be useful to ask students what their congruent pairs and arguments tell about the segments and angles of any rectangle and about those determined when diagonals are drawn in a rectangle. Some possible observations might include things like this:

- Opposite sides are congruent and parallel.
- Corner angles are right angles.
- Diagonals bisect each other (cut each other into two equal pieces).
- Angles formed where the diagonals meet are congruent in opposite pairs.
- Diagonals act as transversals connecting the pairs of parallel lines formed by opposite sides of the rectangle. The angles on opposite sides of these transversals are congruent in pairs (e.g. $\angle PQT \cong \angle RST$). We don't expect students to use terms like *transversal* and *alternate interior angles* at this point, though they might recall these relationships from their work with *Shapes and Designs*.
- The diagonals of a rectangle are congruent.

3.2 Congruent Triangles

Mathematical Goals

- Connect the notions of symmetry transformations to an informal strategy for checking to see whether given figures are congruent
- Develop ability to match corresponding parts of congruent figures and to express those correspondences in standard notation
- Use reasoning about symmetry transformations and properties of figures with embedded triangles to deduce further information about given figures

Launch

- *Why are the rectangles in the bridge picture all criss-crossed by diagonals to produce four triangles?*

If students do not recall the work with polystrips, demonstrate the strips and the basic principle of rigidity of triangles.

Pose question A of Problem 3.2. Give students a few minutes to make a conjecture about the number of triangles in the figure. Ask:

- *Which seem to be exactly the same shape and size?*
- *Your task in the problem is to find pairs of triangles that you think are congruent and find ways to justify your answers.*

Give them a start by showing how to write their claim in correct notation and guide them through an argument for why the pair is congruent. "For $\triangle PTS \cong \triangle QTR$, the rectangle is symmetric about a vertical line through its center, so that a reflection transformation would flip P to Q, S to R, and T to itself. That means that $\triangle PTS$ will map onto $\triangle QTR$, so the triangles are congruent."

Arrange students in pairs or groups to work on the problem.

Materials

- Transparency 3.2
- Mirrors or transparent reflecting tools
- Rulers, angle rulers, or protractors
- Tracing paper
- polystrips (optional—see Labsheet 3.4A)

Explore

Watch to see that students record with correct notation and that, after using their eyes to spot potential congruent triangles, they are developing transformation arguments to explain why the proposed triangles in each pair could be matched *face to face*.

Note that it is possible to propose $\triangle PTQ \cong \triangle RTS$. This congruence would be checked by a half-turn rotation about point T, since the statement identifies P and R as corresponding vertices.

Materials

- Labsheet 3.2

Generate a class list of congruent triangle pairs. Again, be careful to check the correspondences of vertices indicated by the proposed notation. For example, a claim like $\triangle PQT \cong \triangle STR$ has not followed the standard notational convention.

Have a large copy of the overall figure and of the three basic triangle parts of the figure.

Make a list of observations about the rectangle they made while justifying their results, for example:

Opposite sides are congruent and parallel.

Corner angles are right angles. Etc…

Materials
- Student notebooks

Vocabulary
- diagonals

ACE Assignment Guide for Problem 3.2

Core 5, 6, 19–23

Adapted For suggestions about adapting ACE exercises, see the CMP *Special Needs Handbook*. **Connecting to Prior Units** 19–23 *Covering and Surrounding*

Answers to Problem 3.2

A. These triangles are embedded in the figure: $\triangle PTQ$, $\triangle QTR$, $\triangle RTS$, $\triangle PTS$, $\triangle PRQ$, $\triangle RPS$, $\triangle SQR$, and $\triangle QSP$.

B. The reflection symmetries are: A reflection in a vertical line through the midpoints of $\overline{PQ}$ and $\overline{SR}$ (and point T); a reflection through a horizontal line through the midpoints of $\overline{PS}$ and $\overline{QR}$ (and point T). The rotation symmetry is: 180° rotation about point T.

There are no translation symmetries in the figure.

C. Pairs that are congruent include:

$\triangle PTQ \cong \triangle RTS$

$\triangle PTS \cong \triangle QTR$

$\triangle PRS \cong \triangle PQR$

$\triangle PRS \cong \triangle QSR$

$\triangle PRS \cong \triangle PQS$

$\triangle PQR \cong \triangle QSR$

$\triangle PQR \cong \triangle PQS$

$\triangle PQS \cong \triangle QSR$

D. The transformations that match corresponding vertices of congruent triangles will all be either reflections in horizontal or vertical lines through the center of the rectangle or half-turns (180° rotations) about point T. For example, to map $\triangle PQT$ onto $\triangle RTS$, the half-turn is required. To map $\triangle PQS \cong \triangle SRP$, reflection about the horizontal line is required. Mapping $\triangle PQS$ to $\triangle RSQ$ would require a 180° rotation around point T.

E. To check whether the proposed triangles are congruent, one would like to know that the lengths of sides $\overline{PT}, \overline{TQ}, \overline{PQ}, \overline{RT}, \overline{TS}$, and $\overline{SR}$ and whether the various angles involved in the two triangles are congruent. For example you would want to know things such as: is $\angle PTQ \cong \angle RTS$? Is $\angle PQT \cong \angle RST$? etc. Since the rectangle has 180° rotation symmetry around T, you can argue that the parts of triangles of interest are in fact congruent.

The Matching Game

Goals

- Develop ability to match corresponding parts of congruent figures and to express those correspondences in standard notation

- Discover minimal conditions about corresponding sides and angles of triangles from which one can infer congruence of the two figures—SAS, ASA, SSS

This investigation engages students in a game we call the Matching Game. Experiences in this game lead students from analysis of game strategy to discovery of the Angle-Side-Angle, Side-Side-Side, and Side-Angle-Side congruence principles. Rules for the Matching Game are in the student text. A collection of challenge figure templates appear in the blackline masters accompanying these teacher notes.

The idea of the Matching Game is to have the members of each team separated by some sort of visual barrier, so that the team member who will draw the directed figure will not be able to see the figure he/she is being asked to replicate. The first team member knows the measures of sides and angles of the challenge figure and communicates key information (one step at a time) to his/her partner. When the team believes it has the required copy drawn, their opponents check to see that it matches the challenge figure. If it does not, the drawing team loses the maximum of six points and play swings to the other team.

Usually after only a few rounds of the game, students will realize that they can give minimal directions to their partners and still communicate the exact triangular shape they have in mind. However, you will need to ask questions so that they will also realize that not just any set of three triangle measurements will suffice. The specific questions in Problem 3.3 are planned to help students articulate their ideas about which combinations of side and angle measurements are necessary and sufficient to determine the shape of a triangle.

Launch 3.3

To begin work on this problem it is useful to explain the general object of the game (communicating drawing rules for triangles) and to read through the given rules. Since some student(s) might quickly sense the kinds of drawing directions that will be optimal, you can simply pose the Getting Ready question and advise teams to put their heads together to think about it without revealing their ideas to other teams who will be their competitors. Then have the teams play at least one round of the game until a winner (or tie if that occurs) is determined in each pairing. As the game proceeds, monitor the way play is going to clarify rules and to see that the game is being played as intended.

To turn student attention from actually playing the game to analyzing strategies and articulating the geometric principles behind strategies, ask various teams to share their strategies and their answers to the overall question for the problem,

Suggested Questions

- *"How much information about two triangles will guarantee that they are congruent?"*

In response to answers like "Just three things" you might ask

- *Any three things?*

- *Will that number always be necessary, or can you get by with less?*

If someone suggests a number like six, ask if anyone thinks you can get by with less.

Ask students to work on the questions in Problem 3.3 and as they work to sharpen their ideas about the "How many pieces of information?" question.

Arrange students in groups of four to play the game.

Explore 3.3

As students work on the questions, check to see that they are addressing Question A, part (3) (in case they focus on SAS or ASA only).

As students work on Question B, you will need to keep an eye out to see that students are thinking about all the possible ways that the given directions might be interpreted. If students think the answer to part (1) is "yes", draw a triangle that has these three angles but sides that are twice as long.

Suggested Questions

- *Are these two triangles congruent?* (No.)

- *How do they fail to be congruent?* (The one you drew is too large.)

- *What relationship do the triangles have?* (They are similar, same shape but not necessarily the same size.)

If students think that the answer to Question B, part (2) is "no", prod them to reconsider.

- *What seems to be missing?* (You need either the measure of BC so that ∠C can be located, or more effectively, you need to find the measure of ∠A (180° − 100° − 45°) so that the direction of side $\overline{AC}$ can be fixed.)

- *Could you figure out what you need from what is given?* (Since the sum of the angles of a triangle is 180°, you can subtract the sum of the two angles given to get the missing angle.)

Question B, part (4) foreshadows the Side-Side-Side congruence condition. With only a ruler for length and a measuring device for angles, it is not easy to use information about three sides to draw a triangle. The standard device is to draw one side (say $\overline{AB}$ = 5) and then use a compass to swing arcs (from A of radius 3.6 and from B of radius 2.9) to locate the third vertex.

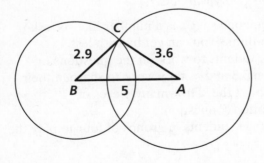

Question D uses what students have learned about triangles to look at a figure that is made of three triangles. Students will need to see that if they begin by looking at one of the triangles, they will need at least three measures to reproduce it accurately. Then they have one measure, a side, for

the adjacent triangle, so only two more will be needed for that triangle. Now you have a measure, a side, for the third triangle and two more will be needed. This means that you need a minimum of seven measures altogether. If students think that 5 sides of the polygon are enough (without the diagonals), you might have them check by constructing a pentagon with polystrips, given only five sides. This results in a non-rigid figure with variable angles. How do we fix this problem? With the diagonals.

Summarize 3.3

The summary involves several key ideas so it is worth getting group reports on each question and discussing each until there is consensus about the result. This may mean planning for one day for work on the problem exploration and an additional day for summary of results.

The answers to questions in A will probably come fairly easily. It will be useful to have a large picture or overhead display of challenge figure 1 visible for students to refer to or point to as they present their ideas.

The answers to questions in B will be more uncertain and students should be encouraged to come to a board or overhead display to demonstrate their reasoning (for example, to make a sketch showing how two different size triangles could have the same angle measure combinations). They have had some experience with this in *Stretching and Shrinking*.

At each stage in the responses to the parts of this problem, students should be asked to explain how they know they are right, not simply to give yes/no answers. Students should, by now in CMP, know that they must always be ready with explanations of their reasoning.

Question C asks students to summarize what they found from parts A and B. You may want to summarize on chart paper that can be hung in the classroom for several days.

Question D asks students to move beyond their thinking with triangles, to examine a pentagon with two diagonals drawn from the same vertex. This means the pentagon has been triangulated. Here the new thing students need to see is that by focusing on the triangles, they can deduce a minimum set of measures needed to reproduce the figure by using what they know about triangles.

3.3

The Matching Game

Mathematical Goals

- Develop ability to match corresponding parts of congruent figures and to express those correspondences in standard notation
- Discover minimal conditions about corresponding sides and angles of triangles from which one can infer congruence of the two figures—SAS, ASA, SSS

Launch

Explain the general object of the game (communicating drawing rules for triangles) and to read through the given rules. Pose the Getting Ready question and advise teams to put their heads together to think about it without revealing their ideas to other teams who will be their competitors. Then have the teams play at least one round of the game until a winner (or tie if that occurs) is determined in each pairing.

Ask students to work on the questions in Problem 3.3 and as they work to sharpen their ideas about the "How many pieces of information?" question.

Arrange students in groups of four to play the game.

Materials

- Transparency 3.3A and 3.3B
- Mirrors or transparent reflecting tools
- Tracing paper
- Rulers
- Angle rulers or protractors

Explore

If students think the answer to Question B, part (1) is "yes", draw a triangle that has these three angles but sides that are twice as long.

- *Are these two triangles congruent?*
- *How do they fail to be congruent? What relationship do the triangles have?*

If students think that the answer to Question B, part (2) is "no", prod them to reconsider by asking,

- *What seems to be missing? Could you figure out what you need from what is given?*

In Question D be sure to push students to relate their ideas to triangulation of a figure from a single vertex so that they can use what they know about triangles to find out about other figures.

Materials

- Labsheet 3.3
- Rulers
- Angle rulers or protractors

Summarize

Have groups report on each question and discuss each until there is fairly wide consensus about the results.

Answers to Question B need to be demonstrated.

As students report, ask how they know they are correct.

Summarize ideas and results on chart paper to hang in the classroom for as long as needed.

Materials

- Student notebooks

ACE Assignment Guide
for Problem 3.3

Core 7–10

Other *Extensions* 27–29; unassigned choices from previous problems

Adapted For suggestions about adapting ACE exercises, see the CMP *Special Needs Handbook*.

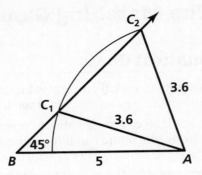

Answers to Problem 3.3

A. Game Strategy

1. The drawing directions for Challenge Figure 1 can be completed in a variety of ways, but the most efficient method would be to indicate either "Draw an angle of 18° at point Y" or "Mark a point Z on the other side of angle X so that $\overline{XZ} = 1.75$ inches."

2. The directions in Part (1) would both cost 3 points.

3. Many different lists of directions will work at a cost of only 3 points. Any Angle-Side-Angle or Side-Angle-Side combination will be sufficient to determine the triangle. Each will cost 3 points.

4. Fewest number of points is always 3.

B. Direction Set 1: Three angles are not enough to determine the size of the required triangle. Three angles give a similar figure.

Direction Set 2: From the given angle information you can deduce that the remaining angle measures 35° and then you have Angle-Side-Angle information and can draw the triangle.

Direction Set 3: There are two possible triangles that meet the given conditions. The following sketch shows how they could be determined, by drawing an arc of radius 3.6 centered at A and noticing the two places where that arc intersects the ray of angle B (in this case at C_1 and C_2).

We don't expect this kind of reasoning from students, but some rough sketches should be sufficient to reveal the double possibilities with the given conditions.

Direction Set 4: Although there is only one triangle with three given side lengths (as long as the sum of any two is greater than the third), students might not easily find a strategy for using that information to draw a triangle. As we commented above, the standard construction involves use of compass arcs. The general question of whether three side lengths determine a unique triangle can be put off until Problem 3.4 where it is addressed head-on.

C. Based on the explorations of this problem, the minimal information needed to be sure that two triangles are congruent would consist of either: (1) Two sides and the angle included by them; (2) Two angles and their common side; (3) Three sides.

D. Students will need to see that if they begin by looking at one of the triangles, they will need at least three measures to reproduce it accurately. Then since the adjacent triangle shares a side, they would have the measure of a side and only two more will be needed for that second triangle. Similarly you have a measure (a side) for the third triangle and two more will be needed. This means that you need a minimum of seven measures altogether. This is larger than most students anticipate.

3.4 Polystrip Triangles and Quadrilaterals

Goals

- Use minimal conditions about corresponding sides and angles of triangles from which one can infer congruence of the two figures—SAS, ASA, SSS

- Recognize that these conditions for triangles do not extend to other shapes, in particular quadrilaterals

This problem will work much better if students have actual polystrips to manipulate and test their ideas. See the *Shapes and Designs* teacher to borrow that tool.

Launch 3.4

You might want to demonstrate how the strips can be connected with clasps to form various kinds of figures—build a pentagon or hexagon for the demonstration so that quadrilaterals and triangles are saved for the investigation. Remind students that lengths of sides are measured using distances between holes, not numbers of holes.

Ask students if they recall using the polystrip tool to experiment with whether three given numbers can be used as sides of a triangle.

Then pose the key questions of the problem:

Suggested Questions

- *Do you think that any three numbers can be used as side lengths to form a triangle?*

- *Can three given numbers lead to different (non-congruent) triangles?*

- *What is the situation with quadrilaterals? Do you think that given any four numbers you will all make the same quadrilateral?*

If some students are pretty sure they know the answers to these questions, challenge them to prepare polystrip figures that demonstrate their ideas.

Point out Questions D and E about playing the Matching Game with four-sided figures and suggest that when students get to those that they should use the polystrips and their angle rulers to prepare demonstrations of their ideas.

Arrange students in groups of four to work on the problem.

Explore 3.4

As students work through the questions of this problem, watch to see that each group is recording its conclusions—with sketches and explanations in words—in preparation for the summary class discussion.

On Questions D and E, urge students to see how many different ways they can give directions for the required drawings.

Suggested Question

On the figures of Question E, in particular, you might suggest:

- *Suppose the rules allowed you to say the kind of figure that is being drawn, like 'Draw a rectangle' or 'draw a parallelogram.' How many additional directions would be needed in that case?* (If students recall properties of rectangles and parallelograms, they will need to give fewer drawing clues, because the drawer can use the fact that opposite sides are parallel, adjacent angles are supplementary, and so on.)

Summarize 3.4

In class discussion of Question A, ask students to show polystrip figures that meet the given conditions. Then hold another example in a somewhat different position and ask students why that doesn't show a *different* triangle.

In discussion of Question B, be sure to highlight the flexibility of quadrilaterals and connect this observation back to the earlier work with diagonals in rectangles (Problem 3.2) that appear in constructed figures like the George Washington Bridge that was pictured there. The diagonals effectively brace rectangles by forming four rigid triangles. You might ask whether it would be possible to make a rectangle rigid without drawing in both diagonals. (You can put in one diagonal and the figure becomes rigid. With polystrips students can insert a brace and see this.)

In Question C be sure that students realize how different triangles are from quadrilaterals. In both parts (1) and (2), triangles are completely determined by the three side lengths. Whereas, there are infinitely many quadrilaterals with different shapes that have the same four side lengths.

In discussion of Question D be sure to ask students whether there is more than one way to give the required directions and how they know that five pieces of information will always be enough to draw a quadrilateral (but not just any five pieces of information).

When you come to Question E, you might want to ask the whole class to consider what they could do if the first clue was "the figure is a rectangle" or "the figure is a parallelogram".

Suggested Question

- *How does that reduce the number of additional clues required and why?*

Going Further

Students explored a pentagon in 3.2. You might want to intrigue some students by a question like this:

Suggested Questions

- *If drawing a triangle requires three pieces of side and angle information (SSS, SAS, SAA, or ASA, but not SSA) and drawing a quadrilateral requires 5 pieces of side and angle information, how many pieces of information do you think will be required to specify the shape and size of a pentagon? How about a hexagon? How about an n-gon?* (Figure 1)

Each time we add a side, we actually make a new triangle, which has one side already fixed. So we need an additional two pieces of information (two angles or two sides or an angle and one side to fix the last vertex. Following this pattern, the number of pieces of information is $2n - 3$, where n is the number of sides.

Figure 1

Number of Sides	3	4	5
Number of Diagonals From One	0	1	2
Number of Triangles Formed	1	2	3
Number of Pieces of Information	3	3 + 2	3 + 2 + 2

3.4 Polystrip Triangles and Quadrilaterals

Mathematical Goals

- Use minimal conditions about corresponding sides and angles of triangles from which one can infer congruence of the two figures—SAS, ASA, SSS
- Recognize that these conditions for triangles do not extend to other shapes, in particular quadrilaterals

Launch

Make a pentagon or a hexagon to demonstrate using the strips. Then pose the key questions of the problem:

- *Do you think that any three numbers can be used as side lengths to form a triangle? Can three given numbers lead to different (non-congruent) triangles?*

- *What is the situation with quadrilaterals? Do you think that given any four numbers you will all make the same quadrilateral?*

If some students feel they know the answers, challenge them to prepare polystrip figures that demonstrate their ideas.

Point out the Questions D and E about playing the Match Game with four-sided challenge figures and suggest that when students get to those that they should use the polystrips and their angle rulers to prepare demonstrations of their ideas.

Arrange students in groups of four to work on the problem.

Materials
- Labsheet 3.4A
- Transparency 3.4
- Mirrors or transparent reflecting tools
- Rulers, angle rulers, or protractors
- Polystrips
- Tracing paper

Explore

On Questions D and E, urge students to see how many different ways they can give directions for the required drawings. On the figures of Question E, in particular, you might suggest something like this,

- *Suppose the rules allowed you to say the kind of figure that is being drawn, like 'Draw a rectangle' or 'draw a parallelogram.' How many additional directions would be needed in that case?*

Materials
- Labsheet 3.4
- Rulers, angle rulers, or protractors

Summarize

In class discussion of Question A, ask students to show polystrip figures that meet the given conditions. In Question B, highlight the flexibility of quadrilaterals and connect this observation back to the earlier work with diagonals in rectangles (Problem 3.2. The diagonals brace rectangles by forming four rigid triangles.)

In Question C, triangles are completely determined by the three side lengths. Whereas, there are infinitely many quadrilaterals with different shapes that have the same four side lengths.

Materials
- Student notebooks

Vocabulary
- polystrips

continued on next page

In Question D, be sure to ask students whether there is more than one way to give the required directions and how they know that five pieces of information will always be enough to draw a quadrilateral (but not just any five pieces of information).

When you come to Question E, you might want to ask the whole class to consider what they could do if the first clue was "the figure is a rectangle" or "the figure is a parallelogram".

- *How does that reduce the number of additional clues required and why?*

See the extended Summarize for a Going Further.

ACE Assignment Guide for Problem 3.4

Differentiated Instruction
Solutions for All Learners

Core 11–14, 24
Other *Applications* 15, 16; *Connections* 25, 26; unassigned choices from previous problems

Adapted For suggestions about adapting ACE exercises, see the CMP *Special Needs Handbook*.
Connecting to Prior Units 24: *Filling and Wrapping*; 25: *Stretching and Shrinking*

Answers to Problem 3.4

A. Triangles
   1. one
   2. one
   3. none (5 + 10 < 20)
   4. one
B. Quadrilaterals
   1. Many quadrilaterals are possible because the angle sizes are not fixed, but all will be parallelograms—illustrating the geometry theorem that if opposite sides of a quadrilateral are congruent, the figure must be a parallelogram.
   2. none (5 + 5 + 5 < 20).

3. Many are possible, but all will either be reflection symmetric kites or arrowheads like those shown below.
(Note: This illustrates the geometry principle that the locus of points equidistant from two given points is the perpendicular bisector of the segment joining those points.)

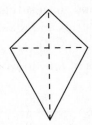

C. 1. Information about sides will completely determine the shape and size of a triangle. However, information about side lengths does not completely determine the shape of a quadrilateral. It does, of course, determine the perimeter, but not the area, as one can see by skewing a rectangle into the shape of a parallelogram with the same base but smaller height.

   2. Yes

   3. No; a quadrilateral with side lengths 3, 4, 3, and 4 in that order could give infinitely many possibilities because the angles are not fixed.

D. Efficient directions for drawing Figure 3 can be given by specifying lengths of two adjacent sides and the three angles containing those sides or by specifying lengths of three adjacent sides and the two angles determined by those sides. In each case, all that will remain to complete the drawing is to connect the ends of the outside edges. Looking at combinations that will not work is instructive. For example, if we know that $\angle A = 122°$, $\angle B = 65°$, $\angle C = 135°$, (from which we can deduce that $\angle D = 38°$) and that $\overline{AD} = 4$ inches, it might seem that we have enough to fix the size. However, we can still draw many different quadrilaterals with these angles and this one given side see illustration below. Not only are the quadrilaterals not congruent, they are not even similar. (Figures 2 and 3)

E. Without specifying that Figure 4 is a rectangle, one would still have to give 5 pieces of side and angle information as in Question D. (However, if one is allowed to give the rectangle clue first, then only two more facts are needed—the side lengths.) In the case of Figure 5, only 5 pieces of side and angle information are needed. (However, if one is allowed to give the parallelogram clue first then only 3 pieces of information are needed.)

F. In general, one needs five pieces of information about sides and angles of a quadrilateral for a drawing to be made, with certainty that it will be congruent to the original figure.

Figure 2

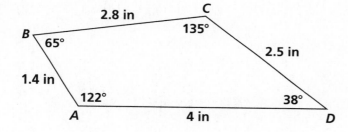

Figure 3

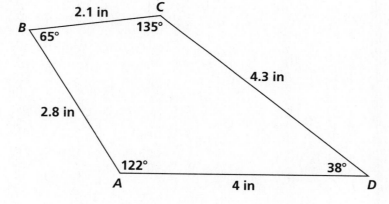

Investigation 3

ACE
Assignment Choices

Differentiated Instruction
Solutions for All Learners

Problem 3.1
Core ACE 1–4, 17, 18

Problem 3.2
Core ACE 5–6, 19–23

Problem 3.3
Core ACE 7–10
Other *Extensions* 27–29; unassigned choices from previous problems

Problem 3.4
Core ACE 11–14, 24
Other ACE 15, 16, 25, 26, and unassigned choices from previous problems

Adapted For suggestions about adapting Exercises 1–4 and other ACE exercises, see the CMP *Special Needs Handbook*.
Connecting to Prior Units 17–23: *Covering and Surrounding*; 24: *Filling and Wrapping*; 25: *Stretching and Shrinking*

Applications

1. Corresponding Congruent Angles and Sides

Angles		Sides	
A	L	$\overline{AB}$	$\overline{LK}$
B	K	$\overline{BC}$	$\overline{KN}$
C	N	$\overline{CD}$	$\overline{NM}$
D	M	$\overline{DA}$	$\overline{ML}$

2. Corresponding Congruent Angles and Sides

Angles		Sides	
E	R	$\overline{EF}$	$\overline{RP}$
F	P	$\overline{FG}$	$\overline{PQ}$
G	Q	$\overline{GE}$	$\overline{QR}$

3. Corresponding Congruent Angles and Sides

Angles		Sides	
S	X	$\overline{ST}$	$\overline{XZ}$
T	Z	$\overline{SU}$	$\overline{XY}$
U	Y	$\overline{TU}$	$\overline{ZY}$

4. Corresponding Congruent Angles and Sides

Angles		Sides	
A	R	$\overline{AB}$	$\overline{RS}$
B	S	$\overline{BC}$	$\overline{ST}$
C	T	$\overline{CD}$	$\overline{TP}$
D	P	$\overline{DE}$	$\overline{PQ}$
E	Q	$\overline{EA}$	$\overline{QR}$

5. a. The rectangle has 2 lines of symmetry, through midpoints of opposite sides, and 180° rotation symmetry around N.

b. (Figure 4)

Figure 4   **Rectangle *JKLM* and Its Congruent Triangles**

Sets of Congruent Triangles	Evidence for Congruence
△*JNM* and △*KNL*	Since *JKLM* has reflection symmetry in a vertical line through the center, the vertices of △*JNM* and △*KNL* will match up after this reflection.
△*MJL* and △*LKM* △*JKL* and △*KJM*	Since *JKLM* has reflection symmetry in a vertical line through the center, the vertices of △*MJL* and △*LKM* will match up after this reflection. Similarly for △*JKL* and △*KJM*.
△*MNL* and △*JNK*	Since *JKLM* has reflection symmetry in a horizontal line through the center, the vertices of △*MNL* and △*JNK* will match up after this reflection.
△*MJL* and △*KLJ* △*MJK* and △*KLM*	Since *JKLM* has 180° rotation symmetry about its center, the vertices of △*MJL* and △*KLJ* will match up after the rotation. Similarly for △*MJK* and △*KLM*.
△*MJK* and △*JML* △*JKL* and △*MLK*	Since *JKLM* has reflection symmetry in a horizontal line through the center, the vertices of △*MJK* and △*JML* will match up after the reflection. Similarly for △*JKL* and △*MLK*. **Or** Can be reasoned through arguments like if △*MJK* and △*LKJ* are congruent and △*LKJ* and △*JML* are congruent then △*MJK* and △*JML* are congruent since they are both congruent to the same triangle △*LKJ*.

6. **a.** The lines of symmetry are the diagonals $\overline{VX}$ and $\overline{WY}$. The figure has 180° rotation symmetry about Z.

   b. (Figure 5)

7. Possibly congruent (no side lengths given)

8. $\angle E$ does not correspond with given $\angle C$. $\angle F$ needs to be 40° to match; instead it is 30°.

9. Congruent. The Pythagorean Theorem gives us the third side, so we have Side-Side-Side.

10. Congruent, by Side-Angle-Side.

11. Answers will vary. Possible answer: A rectangle with sides that are 10 cm and 3 cm.

12. Answers will vary. Possible answer: A rhombus with side lengths of 12.2 cm and an angle measuring 60 degrees.

13. Answers will vary. Possible answer: A right triangle with legs of length 12 cm and 16 cm

14. D

15. **a.** Students might use the Pythagorean Theorem to find the 3rd side, and then compare the triangles using the side-side-side condition. Or, they might say that the triangles are congruent using side-right angle-side. Or, they might say that the y-axis is a line of symmetry so $C{\to}B$ and $A{\to}A$ and $O{\to}O$, and so the triangles are congruent.

    b. $\overline{AC} = \overline{AB}$ because these are corresponding sides of congruent triangles. $\angle CAO \cong \angle BAO$, because these are corresponding angles of congruent triangles, etc.

16. **a.** Students might use the Pythagorean Theorem to find lengths of $\overline{PS}$ and $\overline{QR}$. Or, they might use the fact that the y-axis is a line of symmetry to match the two sides.

    b. The x-axis is a line of symmetry for the isosceles trapezoid so base angles $\angle PSR$ and $\angle QRS$ are equal. Students may also argue that the quadrilaterals formed by the y-axis cutting the trapezoid are congruent since all the sides are equal in length which can be shown using the coordinates.

Connections

17. Congruent; we know that $\frac{1}{2}$ of a diameter is the radius, and $\frac{1}{2}$ of 6 is 3.

18. Not congruent; the area of the first circle is 55.39 cm^2 and $55.39 \neq 58.69$.

19. Perimeters: 30 cm, 34 cm
    Areas: 36 cm^2 for each
    The two quadrilaterals are not congruent.

20. Perimeters: 56 cm for each
    Areas: 84 cm^2 for each; congruent

21. Perimeters: 4π (about 12.56 cm); Areas: 4π cm^2 (about 12.56 cm^2) congruent

22. Shapes that are congruent have the same perimeter, but having the same perimeter does not ensure congruence.

23. Shapes that are congruent have the same area, but having the same area does not ensure congruence.

Figure 5

Rhombus *VWXY* and Its Congruent Triangles

Sets of Congruent Triangles	Evidence for Congruence
$\triangle VSY \cong \triangle VSW$ $\triangle VSY \cong \triangle XSY$ $\triangle VSW \cong \triangle XSY$ $\triangle VSW \cong \triangle XSW$ $\triangle VWX \cong \triangle VYX$ $\triangle VYW \cong \triangle XYW$	The diagonals of a rhombus are lines of symmetry for the figure so congruent triangles are created.
$\triangle VYX \cong \triangle XWV$ $\triangle XYW \cong \triangle VWY$ $\triangle VSW \cong \triangle XSY$ $\triangle VSY \cong \triangle XSW$	The rhombus has rotation symmetry 180° about the intersection point of its diagonals.

24. a. Regardless of where we slice the sphere, the new surface will always be a circle.

b. She could find the volume for a cylinder with the same dimensions and then multiply that answer by $\frac{2}{3}$ to find the volume of the sphere.

c. $V = \frac{2}{3} \times$ volume of cylinder with same dimensions, so

$$V = \frac{2}{3}(2.5^2\pi) \, 11$$
$$= \frac{137.5\pi}{3} \text{ cm}^3 \approx 144 \text{ cm}^3$$

d. $V = \frac{2}{3}(\pi r^2)h$ where r is the radius of the sphere and h is the diameter, or $V = \frac{4}{3}\pi r^3$.

25. A brace in a quadrilateral is also the diagonal which separates the quadrilateral into two triangles. Since triangles are rigid, the quadrilateral will also be rigid.

26. a.

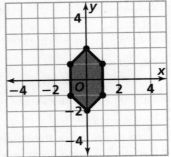

b. $(1.5x, 1.5y)$

c. Yes; Applying a rule with the same factor for the x and y coordinates always generates a similar figure. Alternatively, one can measure corresponding side lengths and angles. The angle measures are equal and the side lengths are proportional, so the figures are similar.

d. The image is similar. The angles are congruent and the side lengths are proportional. Alternatively, adding to the coordinates of a figure affects only its location, not its size. Therefore, doubling both the x and the y coordinates results in a similar figure.

Extensions

27. a. 12 cm

b. Yes, because all side lengths are the same.

28. We also have SAS congruence. No, we can't be certain since we can't calculate the third side.

29. a. Yes. We could abbreviate this condition as side-side-angle.

b. In Exercise 27 we were able to use the Pythagorean Theorem to find a unique length for the 3rd sides of the triangles. Thus, side-side-right angle is equivalent to side-side-side. However, in Exercise 28 we have no right angle and so the Pythagorean Theorem does not apply. In general, side-side-angle information is not sufficient to show that two triangles are congruent.

Possible Answers to Mathematical Reflections

1. Two figures are congruent if one can be moved around or transformed by reflection, translation, and/or rotation to fit exactly on top of the other. All angles in the two figures have the same measure. All sides have the same length. The figures have the same number of sides. Everything is the same except possibly where they are and which direction they are facing.

2. You can show two figures are congruent if you can find some combination of reflections, rotations and translations that transforms the points of one figure to become the corresponding points of the other figure.

3. For triangles you only need to check three parts (but it matters which ones!). For example, if you measure all three sides and find that they are the same length in both triangles, you do not need to measure the angles to know that they are congruent.

Mathematical and Problem-Solving Goals

- Develop the insight and ability to use triangle congruence conditions to deduce unknown side and angle lengths in figures

- Develop basic ability to use triangle congruence principles to prove properties of familiar quadrilaterals

- Learn to appreciate the power of transformational geometry to describe motions, patterns, designs and properties of shapes in the real world

Summary of Problems

Problem 4.1 Finding Distances Without Measuring

Here students use the ideas of congruence developed in Investigation 3 to solve a problem involving congruent triangles in a story context. In so doing, they see the power of inference based on known facts.

Problem 4.2 Using Symmetry to Find Properties of Shapes

Students use what they have learned about symmetry and congruence to solve problems involving polygons. In some cases, students are asked to argue from what is given to find measures of other angles and sides of polygons. In other problems, students reason from what is given and what they can deduce to tell what kind of polygon the shape is.

In some sense, any mathematical proof (or algebraic derivation) is a chain of reasoning that starts from some facts that are known and proceeds to infer some other facts from logical reasoning. One of the tricky aspects of introducing proof in any mathematics course is establishing clearly what is *known to be true*. In a formal geometry course, considerable effort is made to be very clear and precise about those assumptions or axioms. Since students commonly enter that experience with prior knowledge of many geometric *facts*, they usually struggle with the challenge of separating what must be proven from what can be assumed true.

We expect that CMP students will have this difficulty in separating what can be assumed true from what is to be proven true. We make no pretense about establishing a rigorous axiomatic development of geometry from first principles here. Instead, we ask students to assume that they know some key things about lines, angles, and triangles and to use that knowledge to draw some conclusions about specific situations involving triangles and about quadrilaterals.

To make this informal deductive experience work, it will be useful to launch this Investigation by asking students to articulate some key things that they know already.

Suggested Questions

You might prompt this kind of *setting the ground-rules* by a full-class discussion guided by the following questions:

- *In this Investigation we are going to use what we've learned about lines, angles, and triangles to solve problems that involve particular triangles and to show that further deductions about polygons are logical consequences of properties of more basic shapes. To get started, let's summarize the key things we know about lines, angles, and triangles.*

- *What do you know about the measures of angles in any triangle?* (The sum is always 180°.)

- *How do we know the angle sum of a triangle is 180°? Did we prove this?* (We did not prove this. We measured examples in *Shapes and Designs*.)

- *What do you know about the lengths of sides in any triangle?* (The sum of any two is always greater than the third.)

- *What measures should we check to see if two triangles are congruent?* (Angle-Side-Angle, Side-Angle-Side, Side-Side-Side conditions guarantee congruence.)

- *Suppose that you have a right triangle. What do you know about its sides and angles?* (Pythagorean theorem relating sides; non-right angles add to 90°.)

- *What do you know about sides and angles in isosceles and equilateral triangles?* (In isosceles triangles at least two sides are the same length and the base angles are congruent; in equilateral triangles all three angles are 60° and all three sides are the same length.)

- *What do you know about the angles formed when two lines intersect as in the following sketch?* (Opposite angles are congruent in pairs.)

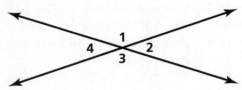

- *What do you know about the angles formed when parallel lines are cut by another line like that shown below?* [Alternate interior angles are congruent; corresponding angles on same side of the transversal are congruent; interior angles on the same side of the transversal are supplementary (students might not recognize these latter two; we need only the first about alternate interior angles). In the labeled sketch that follows, the odd numbered angles are congruent to each other; the even numbered angles are congruent to each other.]

- *Does this sketch have any symmetry?* (Yes, it has rotation symmetry.)

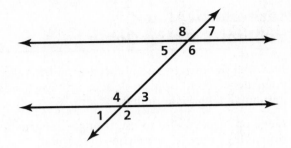

This pattern also works in the opposite direction. If one knows that the angles formed when one line intersects two others are congruent in the ways suggested, then one can conclude that the lines are parallel.

- *What do you know to be true about angle and side measures if you are given a figure that has reflection symmetry?* (Angles or sides that correspond to each other in the reflection line have the same measures.)

- *What do you know to be true about angles and side measures, if you are given a figure that has rotation symmetry?* (Angles or sides that correspond to each other in the rotation have the same measures.)

With this set of common knowledge established, it will be easier to work through the informal proof tasks of this investigation, because the facts that can be used as justifications for claims will be established. You might want to record the results of the class summary and display them in the classroom or even provide a copy for each student as a reference.

	Suggested Pacing	Materials for Students	Materials for Teachers	ACE Assignments
All	$3\frac{1}{2}$ days	Student notebooks, tracing paper (or lightweight plain paper), grid paper, rulers, mirrors, transparent reflection tools, angle rulers or protractors (1 per group)	Blank transparency and transparency markers, overhead graphing calculator, mathematical reflections (all optional)	
4.1	1 day	Labsheets 4.1, 4ACE 8	Transparency 4.1	1–10, 16, 17
4.2	2 days	Labsheets 4.2A, 4.2B	Transparencies 4.2A, 4.2B	11–15, 18–25
MR	$\frac{1}{2}$ day			

Goals

- Develop the insight and ability to use triangle congruence conditions to deduce unknown side and angle lengths in figures

- Learn to appreciate the power of transformational geometry to describe motions, patterns, designs and properties of shapes in the real world

Launch 4.1

As is always the case in problem solving or proof tasks, it is important to establish what is known about the problematic situation. Thus an effective launch of this problem will probably begin with the story and the diagram. After giving students some time to read the story and study the diagram, it will probably be useful to ask someone to explain how they think the engineer constructed the given diagram—what information was used and in what order were the various segments and angles drawn. You might help this process by providing a sketch showing only the river and the location of the two trees.

Of course, there is some information that the engineer must have had but is not mentioned in the set-up story. This situation is typical of those in which assumptions are made, based on a sketch. So, in this case, before revealing that fact or before letting some student discover it and tell the whole class, it makes sense to close the launch phase of work on the problem with a comment something like this:

Suggested Question

- *Your task is to figure out how the engineer figured out the length of the new bridge to be built from point A directly across to point B and to be sure that her reasoning was correct. Answering Questions A–D will help.*

Arrange students in pairs or groups of three to work on the problem.

Explore 4.1

As students work on the specific questions of Problem 4.1, they are likely to make some assumptions that are not justified by the information given in the story. Check on how they are reasoning and prod them with general probes like "Are you sure?" and "How do you know?"

In particular, it seems most likely that students will assume that $\angle A$ and $\angle E$ are right angles because they look like they are 90°. While they can reason directly from the engineer's notes about $\angle A$ is right. They can not just say that $\angle E$ is also right. They might also assume that $\overline{AB} \cong \overline{ED}$ because they look like they are the same length in the diagram. The only things that one can know for sure from the story are that $\angle ACB \cong \angle ECD$ (because the angles formed when two lines intersect are congruent in opposite pairs) and that $\overline{BC} \cong \overline{DC}$ (because the old bridge cable was used to mark off segment $\overline{CD}$.)

Summarize 4.1

When students seem ready to share their thinking about the questions of this problem, it will probably help to have a large sketch displayed on the board or on an overhead transparency for reference.

As students give their answers to the series of questions, it is important to probe their reasoning to see how they can justify their claims based on information in the story or facts about lines, angles, and triangles from the list of *ground rules* established as a basis for reasoning in this investigation.

Finding Distances Without Measuring

Mathematical Goals

- Develop the insight and ability to use triangle congruence conditions to deduce unknown side and angle lengths in figures
- Learn to appreciate the power of transformational geometry to describe motions, patterns, designs and properties of shapes in the real world

Launch

See pages 8 and 9 for a review and summary that can help students take stock of what they know before they work on this problem. Begin with the story and the diagram. After giving students some time to read the story and study the diagram, ask someone to explain how they think the engineer constructed the given diagram—what information was used and in what order were the various segments and angles drawn. Show a sketch showing only the river and the location of the two trees. Arrange students in pairs or threes.

- *Your task is to figure out how the engineer figured out the length of the new bridge to be built from point A directly across to point B and to be sure that her reasoning was correct. Answering Questions A–D will help.*

Materials

- Transparency 4.1
- Mirrors or transparent reflecting tools
- Rules, angle rules, or protractors
- Tracing paper

Explore

Students are likely to make some assumptions that are not justified by the information given in the story.

In particular, it seems most likely that students will assume that $\angle A$ and $\angle E$ are right angles because they look like they are 90°. They can reason from the engineer's notes that $\angle A$ is right but cannot just say that $\angle E$ is also right. They might also assume that $\overline{AB} \cong \overline{ED}$ because they look like they are the same length in the diagram. The only things that one can know for sure from the story are that $\angle ACB \cong \angle ECD$ (because the angles formed when two lines intersect are congruent in opposite pairs) and that $\overline{BC} \cong \overline{DC}$ (because the old bridge cable was used to mark off $\overline{CD}$).

Materials

- Labsheet 4.1

Summarize

It may help to have a large sketch displayed on the board or on an overhead transparency for reference. As students give their answers to the series of questions, it is important to probe their reasoning to see how they can justify their claims based on information in the story or facts about lines, angles, and triangles from the list of *ground rules* established as a basis for reasoning in this investigation.

Materials

- Student notebooks

ACE Assignment Guide for Problem 4.1

Core 1–10, 16
Other Connections 17; unassigned choices from previous problems
Labsheet 4ACE Exercise 8 is provided if Exercise 8 is assigned

Adapted For suggestions about adapting Exercise 9 and other ACE exercises, see the CMP *Special Needs Handbook*.
Connecting to Prior Units 16: *Stretching and Shrinking*; 17: *Looking for Pythagoras*

Answers to Problem 4.1

A. As noted above, the only things that one can know for sure from the story are that $\angle ACB \cong \angle ECD$ (because the angles formed when two lines intersect are congruent in opposite pairs) and that $\overline{BC} \cong \overline{DC}$. (The old bridge cable was used to mark off $\overline{CD}$.)

B. No; she still needs another corresponding congruent side or angle to provide proof of congruency.

The way the story unfolds, there are at least two possible pieces of information that the engineer might have used to provide her with what she needed to be sure the two triangles are congruent.

She might have marked point E so that $\overline{AC} \cong \overline{CE}$ and then connected point E to point D. She could then conclude congruence of the triangles using the Side-Angle-Side criterion.

She might have measured $\angle A$ (it should be 90° to make the distance $\overline{AB}$ as short as possible) and measured $\angle ACB$ and deduced the measure of $\angle B$. Then she could have drawn $\angle CDE$ so that it is congruent to $\angle B$. Congruence of the two triangles would follow by the Angle-Side-Angle criterion. She could have (very inefficiently) tried various positions for point E until she had a position where $\angle CED$ is 90° (to match $\angle A$). This would give her Angle-Angle-Side criterion.

The key issue here is to push students to try to figure out how one could be sure the triangles are congruent and then to see whether the engineer could have known the information needed.

C. Once the triangles are known to be congruent, one only needs to measure segment $\overline{DE}$ and infer (by corresponding parts of congruent triangles) that it is the same length as segment $\overline{AB}$.

D. Yes; One possible answer: A 180° rotation about point C will match the triangles to each other.

4.2 Using Symmetry to Find Properties of Shapes

Goals

- Learn to appreciate the power of transformational geometry to describe motions, patterns, designs and properties of shapes in the real world

This problem is important because we are asking students to pull together knowledge from many different sources. They will need to remember the Pythagorean theorem as well as information about parallelograms and isosceles triangles. This is a place where students can see the accumulation of their mathematical information and ideas. This problem is also important because it foreshadows future work in high school geometry.

Launch 4.2

Ask the class to think about shapes that have reflection and rotation symmetry. Ask some students to draw their shapes on the board.

Suggested Questions

- *What kinds of triangles have reflection symmetry?* (Isosceles and equilateral triangles both do.)

Ask someone to draw an equilateral triangle on the board with its lines of symmetry.

- *How do you know these are lines of symmetry?* (Students may have used transparencies, tracing paper, or other reasoning.)
- *Does this figure have rotation symmetry? (Yes.)*
- *What are the rotation symmetries? Where is the center of rotation?* (120°, 240°, 360°. The center is at the intersection of the lines of symmetry.)
- *How do you know?* (Students may have used transparencies, tracing paper, or other reasoning.)
- *How is an isosceles triangle different?* (It does not have rotation symmetry, and it only has one line of reflection symmetry.)

Draw a parallelogram on the board.

- *Does this parallelogram have reflection symmetry?* (No.)
- *How do you know?* (There is no line of reflection that will make matching sides.)
- *Does it have rotation symmetry?* (Yes.)
- *How do you know?* (If you use the point that is the intersection of the two diagonals as the center, a 180° turn matches the parallelogram to itself.)

In Problem 4.2, you are going to use symmetry *clues* and what you know about congruence to figure out lots of information about polygons. You may also need to use the facts we established prior to 4.1.

Talk about the problem with the students so that they understand what is expected of them. Make clear that they will be asked to give evidence to support their answers to each part of the problem during the summary.

Have students work individually at first, then check their work with their partners, and finally discuss what they have found with a group of four.

Explore 4.2

Circulate as groups work, asking questions to assess their understanding.

Suggested Questions

- *What information does the line of symmetry give you about the lengths of the sides of the triangle?*
- *What information does the line of symmetry give you about the angles in the drawing?*
- *What can you say about triangles ACM and ABM in Question A?*
- *What information does the rotation symmetry of the quadrilateral in Question C give you about the lengths and angles in the drawing?*
- *What can you say about Triangles PRS and PRQ?*

- *In Question D, how do triangles 1 and 2 relate to each other? Label each vertex in a transformation to show what it is the image of. For example, label the image of X as X' and the image of X' as X".*

Summarize 4.2

Put a picture of the triangle in Problem 4.2 up for students—either on the board or on the overhead projector.

Suggested Questions

- *We agreed that this figure has one line of symmetry. How does that information help us figure out more information about the triangle?* (We know that C is the image of B, so the line of symmetry bisects $\overline{CB}$ and is perpendicular to $\overline{CB}$. This tells us $\overline{CM}$ and $\overline{MB}$ both have length 3. We also know that $\angle MAB$ is 37°, $\angle AMC = \angle BMA = 90°$. We know that triangles AMC and AMB are congruent.)

Call on some groups to explain how they used transformations to make the quadrilateral within the circle in Question B.

- *What can you say about the quadrilateral that you made inside the circle?* (Since each of the base angles of the triangle are 45°, each of the angles of the quadrilateral are 90°. Since the four sides of the quadrilateral are all equal to the base of the triangle, the figure has four sides all the same length and right angles. Therefore, it is a square.)

Put a picture of the quadrilateral in Question C up for students.

- *This figure has rotation symmetry. What can we deduce from this about the measurements of the quadrilateral?* ($\overline{PQ}$ and $\overline{RS}$ are the same length. $\overline{QR}$ and $\overline{PS}$ are the same length. $\angle SPR$ and $\angle PRQ$ measure 88°. $\angle PSR$ and $\angle PQR$ measure 53°. $\angle PRS$ and $\angle QPR$ measure 39° since the sum of the angles of a triangle measure 180°. Since alternate interior angles are equal, this makes $\overline{PQ}$ and $\overline{RS}$ parallel, and $\overline{QR}$ and $\overline{SP}$ parallel, so we have a parallelogram. Students may not see the parallel lines cut by a transversal, even after

they have found all the necessary alternate interior angles to be congruent. You might put a sketch of the quadrilateral on the board, and extend the sides and diagonal, and ask if that looks familiar.)

- *What can you say about triangles PRS and PQR? What else can you deduce about the sides of this quadrilateral?* ($\triangle PRS \cong \triangle RPQ$, so $\overline{PQ} \cong \overline{RS}$ and $\overline{QR} \cong \overline{SP}$. So opposite sides of this quadrilateral have equal lengths. Students might also notice opposite angles are congruent. These are properties of any parallelogram.)

Question D is an interesting and important problem. If students struggle, you might give students overnight to continue to think about the problem and then summarize it. There are several ways that three transformations can be carried out to line up the three angles of the original triangle around a point so that a straight angle is formed. The goal is to have students try to justify why the last transformation will exactly fill the "gap." In order to do this, students must keep track of equal distances and angles made by each transformation. At this stage we would expect that students would have an intuitive sense that if you perform a set of transformations on $\triangle VWX$ you can see that angles V, W and X lie on a straight line and thus have an angle sum of 180°. We would expect that they will need help to make their reasoning complete and explicit.

Four distinct ways to use transformations are given below. This is not a complete list of all strategies. **Note:** All steps below reference the labels on this picture.

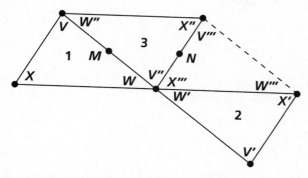

Method 1: Natalie might have reasoned as follows:

Rotate △1 counter clockwise 180° around vertex W, to make △2. Mark the image $V'W'X'$ and note equal sides and angles.

Translate △2 along the line of $\overline{WV}$ (bold in the diagram above, for a distance equal to $\overline{WV}$ to make △3. Mark the image $V''W''X''$, and note equal sides and angles.

Rotate △3 around the mid point N of $\overline{V''X''}$, to fill the *gap*.

The question now is, "Can we be sure that that last transformation exactly filled the gap? It looks like it does, but what do we know from the transformation process that would prove that it does? Here are two ways to reason about this:

A. When △2 is translated all points are moved the same distance ($\overline{WV}$) and direction. So the length of the dashed line (from X' to X'') is the same as $\overline{WV}$ bolded above. Thus we know that the *gap* triangle has 3 sides that exactly match △VWX and so will be congruent to △VWX; so the image of △3 under a rotation around the midpoint N of $\overline{V''X''}$ will fit this gap.

B. When △2 is translated angles are preserved, so ∠W' = ∠W''. This makes $\overline{W'X'}$ parallel to $\overline{W''X''}$. The angle in the gap triangle marked X''' must be congruent to X' (alternate interior angles). We already know that $\overline{W'''X'''}$ is congruent to $\overline{W''X''}$ since translations preserve length. Thus we know that the gap triangle is congruent to the original triangle, by Side-Angle-Side using $\overline{V''X''}$ as the other side.

Method 2:
- Rotate △1 to △2.
- Translate △2 to △3.
- Translate △1 the distance of $\overline{WX}$ to fill the *gap*.

The question is now, "Can we be sure that the last transformation will exactly fill the *gap*?" Here are brief sketches of two ways we might reason about this.

A. When △2 is translated to △3 by a distance of $\overline{WV}$, point X' is moved to X''. So this distance is congruent to $\overline{WV}$. This gives us the three sides of the *gap* triangle congruent to the three sides of the original triangle. So △1 will fit the *gap*.

B. When △2 is translated to △3 angles are preserved so we know $\overline{W'X'}$ is parallel to $\overline{W''X''}$ as above. So the *gap* angle marked X''' must be congruent to X'', as above. Thus the *gap* triangle is congruent to △1, Side-Angle-Side.

Method 3:
- Rotate △1 around the midpoint M of $\overline{VW}$ to make △3.
- Translate △3 along $\overline{VW}$ to make △2.
- Rotate △2 around the midpoint of $\overline{W'X'}$ to fill the *gap*.

Again, we must confirm that this last transformation exactly fills the gap. The reasoning is similar to the above.

Method 4:
- Rotate △1 around midpoint M of $\overline{VW}$
- Rotate △3 around the midpoint N of $\overline{V''X''}$. (△2 is omitted in the reasoning this time.

The question is now, "Do we have a straight angle?" We can show that $\overline{W'X'}$ (on picture above) is parallel to $\overline{W''X''}$ as before. And we know that $\overline{WX}$ is parallel to $\overline{W''X''}$ (alternate interior angles are equal). So $\overline{WX}$ and $\overline{W'X'}$ must form one line, parallel to $\overline{W''X''}$. This gives us the straight angle. (An alternative to this fourth way would be to rotate △1 as above, then translate △1.)

4.2 Using Symmetry to Find Properties of Shapes

Mathematical Goal

• Learn to appreciate the power of transformational geometry to describe motions, patterns, designs and properties of shapes in the real world

Launch

• *What kinds of triangles have reflection symmetry?*

Ask someone to draw an equilateral triangle on the board with its lines of symmetry.

• *How do you know these are lines of symmetry?*
• *Does this figure have rotation symmetry? Where is the center of rotation?*
• *What are the angles of rotation symmetry? How do you know?*
• *How is an isosceles triangle different?*

Draw a parallelogram on the board.

• *Does this parallelogram have reflection symmetry? How do you know? Rotation symmetry? How do you know?*
• *In Problem 4.2, you are going to use symmetry "clues" and what you know about congruence to figure out lots of information about polygons.*

Make it clear that students will be asked to give evidence to support their answers during the summary. Have students work individually at first, then check their work with their partners, and finally discuss what they have found with a group of four.

Materials
• Mirrors or transparent reflecting tools
• Rulers, angle rulers, or protractors
• Tracing paper
• Transparency 4.2A, 4.2B

Explore

Circulate as groups work, asking questions to assess their understanding.

• *What information does the line of symmetry give you about the lengths of the sides of the triangle? About the angles in the drawing?*
• *What can you say about △ACM and △ABM in Question A?*
• *What information does the rotation symmetry of the quadrilateral in Question C give you about the lengths and angles in the drawing?*
• *What can you say about △PRS and △PRQ?*
• *In Question D, how do triangles 1 and 2 relate to each other?*
• *Label each vertex in a transformation to show what it is the image of. For example, label the image of X as X′ and the image of X′ as X″.*

Materials
• Labsheet 4.2A and B
• Labsheet 4ACE 13 (optional)

Display the picture of the triangle in 4.2.

- *This figure has one line of symmetry. How does that information help us find out more about the triangle?*

In Question B, call on groups to explain how they used transformations to make the quadrilateral within the circle.

- *What can you say about the quadrilateral that you made?*

Put a picture of the quadrilateral in Question C up.

- *This figure has rotation symmetry. What can we deduce from this about the measurements of the parallelogram?*

Question D is an important problem. If students struggle, give them overnight to continue to think about the problem. There are several ways that three transformations can be carried out to line up the three angles of the original triangle around a point so that a straight angle is formed. The goal is to have students justify why the last transformation will exactly fill the "gap."

Materials
- Student notebooks

ACE Assignment Guide for Problem 4.2

Differentiated Instruction
Solutions for All Learners

Core 11– 15, 18–21
Other *Connections* 22; *Extensions* 23–25; unassigned choices from previous problems

Adapted For suggestions about adapting Exercise 12 and other ACE exercises, see the CMP *Special Needs Handbook*.
Connecting to Prior Units 19–21: *Looking for Pythagoras*; 22: *Shapes and Designs*

Answers to Problem 4.2

A. Students can use reflection symmetry to deduce that *C* is the image of *B*, so $\overline{CA}$ is the image of $\overline{BA}$, $\angle CAM$ is the image of $\angle BAM$, etc. The measure of $\angle MAB$ is 37°, $\angle AMC = \angle BMA = 90°$, $\overline{MC} = 3$ m, $\overline{MB} = 3$ m, and by the Pythagorean Theorem, $\overline{AC} = \overline{AB} = 5$ m.

B. 1. Possibilities: a series of 90° rotations around the center of the circle; two reflections over the diameters of the circle formed in part by the radii that are sides of the triangle.

2. A square; Since each of the base angles of each of the 4 triangles is 45°, each of the angles of the dashed-lined quadrilateral is $45 + 45 = 90°$. Since the four sides of the

quadrilateral are all equal to the base of the triangle, the figure has four sides of the same length and four right angles.

C. Use rotation symmetry to find corresponding parts.

1. $\overline{SR} = 16$ in., $\overline{QR} = 10$ in., $\angle PSR = 53°$, $\angle QPR = 39°$, $\angle QRP = 88°$, $\angle PRS = 39°$. We can find the measure of $\angle QPR$ because that measure added to 88° and 53° must be 180° since *PQR* is a triangle.

2. $\angle QRP = \angle SPR = 88°$, so $\overline{PS}$ is parallel to $\overline{QR}$. $\angle QPR = \angle SRP = 39°$, so $\overline{PQ}$ is parallel to $\overline{SR}$. The figure has two pairs of opposite sides parallel, so it is a parallelogram.

D. 1 and 2. See the discussion at the end of the Summarize for some possible approaches to this problem.

3. In the finished figure we have angles that are copies of $\angle V$, $\angle X$, and $\angle W$, adjacent to each other at the vertex marked *W*. (These will be marked *W*, *V"*, *X'''*.) These 3 angles form a straight angle. Therefore, $\angle V + \angle X + \angle W = 180°$. This reasoning works for any triangle.

Investigation

ACE
Assignment Choices

Differentiated Instruction
Solutions for All Learners

Problem 4.1
Core 1–10, 16
Other *Connections* 17; unassigned choices from previous problems
Connecting to Prior Units 16: *Stretching and Shrinking*; 17: *Looking for Pythagoras*

Problem 4.2
Core 11–15, 18–21
Other *Connections* 22; *Extensions* 23–25; unassigned choices from previous problems

Adapted For suggestions about adapting Exercises 9 and 12 and other ACE exercises, see the CMP *Special Needs Handbook*.
Connecting to Prior Units 16: *Stretching and Shrinking*; 17, 19: *Looking for Pythagoras*; 22: *Shapes and Designs*

Applications

1. $\triangle ACB \cong \triangle DCE$ by Side-Angle-Side. Since opposite angles of intersecting lines are congruent, $\angle ACB \cong \angle DCE$.

2. Congruent; side-side-side

3. Congruent; side-side-right angle

4. Not enough information

5. Congruent; side-angle-side

6. Not enough information (These two triangles are obviously not congruent, but it relies on a 'measurement' that is very easy to make: the unmarked side is longer on the left-hand triangle than on the right-hand triangle.)

7. Not enough information

8. a. Side $\overline{KN} \cong$ side $\overline{MN}$
   b. $\angle KLN \cong \angle MLN$
   c. $\angle KLN \cong \angle MLN$ and $\angle LNK \cong \angle LNM$

9. By Side ($\overline{PU} \cong \overline{TS}$), Angle ($\angle PUQ \cong \angle STR$ since they are both 90°), Side ($\overline{QU} \cong \overline{RT}$), the triangles are congruent, and therefore the cables are the same length.

10. He needs to ensure that $\angle A$ is a right angle, that C is the midpoint of $\overline{AD}$, that A, C, D are in a straight line, and that B, C, E are in a straight line, and that $\angle D$ is a right angle. Then he can apply the angle-side-angle condition. He can then directly measure $\overline{DE}$ and deduce $\overline{AB}$.

11. a. $\angle MFG \cong \angle MFH$, $\angle FGN \cong \angle HGN$, $\angle H \cong \angle G$, $\angle H \cong \angle F$, so $\angle G \cong \angle F$ and the triangle is equiangular.
    b. $\overline{FH} \cong \overline{FG}$, and $\overline{HG} \cong \overline{FG}$, so $\overline{FH} \cong \overline{HG}$ and the triangle is equilateral.

12. a. The angles are all the same (108°).
    b. The sides are all the same length.
    c. These segments are all the same length.

13. a. Answer will vary. Possible answer: $\triangle XYZ$ was reflected in segment $\overline{XY}$ to position 2. Then $\triangle 2$ was rotated 180° about its midpoint point E to position 3. $\triangle 3$ was rotated 180° to position 4 about point F.

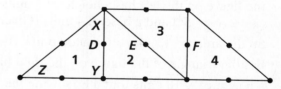

    b. An isosceles trapezoid; Possible reasoning: The figure is a quadrilateral. The top side and the bottom side are parallel since the diagonal in the middle is a transversal and alternate interior angles are congruent. The hypotenuses of $\triangle 1$ and $\triangle 4$ are congruent so the non-parallel sides are congruent.

14. Because $ABCD$ is a square, you know that $\angle ABC \cong \angle BCD$ and that sides $\overline{AB}$, $\overline{BC}$, and $\overline{CD}$ are congruent. Side-Angle-Side shows that $\triangle ABC \cong \triangle BCD$ and therefore $\overline{AC} \cong \overline{BD}$. (**Note:** Students could also use the fact that squares have 90° rotation symmetry

ACE ANSWERS 4

to deduce that the image of one diagonal is the other diagonal.)

15. B

Connections

16. **a.** Triangles ABC and BDE appear to be similar. The engineer would have to know that all the angles need to be the same (in fact she would only need to know 2 angles are the same since the third would automatically be the same by the fact that the sum of the angles of a triangle is 180°)

    b. 150 ft; The distance across the river can be found by noticing that the triangles are similar and are related by a scale factor of 2 (since side $\overline{AC}$ is 200 ft and side $\overline{ED}$ is 400 ft). Since the scale factor is 2, the length of segment $\overline{BE}$ is twice the length of $\overline{BA}$, so $\overline{BA}$ and $\overline{AE}$ are congruent segments. Thus the length of $\overline{AB}$ is 150 ft.

17. The pentagon on the right has a larger area; The top triangles in both pentagons are congruent since they are both 3-4-5 triangles which can be checked using the Pythagorean Theorem. The middle triangles are congruent by SAS since they both have two sides of length 5 and the angle between these sides measures 36°. So all that is left to compare are the areas of the bottom triangles. Using the Pythagorean Theorem, the bottom triangle of the figure on the left has a height of 3 units $(3^2 + 4^2 = 5^2)$ and a base of 4 units (Given). So the area is $\frac{1}{2}(3)(4) = 6$ square units. The bottom triangle of the figure on the right has a height of $\sqrt{10}$ units found by solving the equation $(\sqrt{15})^2 + x^2 = 5^2$. So the area of the bottom triangle is $\frac{1}{2}(\sqrt{10})(\sqrt{15}) \approx 6.12$ square units. So the figure on the right has a larger area.

18. **a.** Yes. $\triangle KRG \cong \triangle KRT$ (Side-Angle-Side) and therefore $\overline{KG} \cong \overline{KT}$ (**Note:** Students could also use the Pythagorean Theorem or reflection symmetry.)

    b. Yes. The same reasoning as Exercise 18, part (a).

    c. Yes. Following on the answers from Exercise 18, part (a) and Exercise 18,

part (b), any triangle constructed using a point on line $\overline{KB}$ will be congruent and consequently the point will be equidistant from the endpoints of $\overline{GT}$.

19. Yes; By the Pythagorean Theorem, the missing side length in the first triangle is $\sqrt{20}$ since $2^2 + 4^2 = (\sqrt{20})^2$. Similarly the missing side length in the second triangle is 4 since $2^2 + 4^2 = (\sqrt{20})^2$. So by SSS, the two triangles are congruent. Also you can use SAS using the right angle and the two legs of the right triangle. (Note to teacher: For right triangles, it is only necessary that the hypotenuse and one of the legs of one triangle is congruent to the hypotenuse and one of the legs of the other triangle to show that they are congruent. This is because the Pythagorean Theorem will determine the second leg uniquely. However students will probably find and compare all three sides and use SSS or use SAS with the two legs and the right angle.)

20. Yes; By ASA the two triangles are congruent since they both have a 90° angle, a 45° angle and the side between the angles is 3.

21. Yes; By ASA the two triangles are congruent. Since the sum of the angles in a triangle is 180° and 90° and 30° are given as measures of the angles in each of the triangles, the third angle must be 60°. Since they both have a 90° angle, a side of length 4 and then a 60° angle in that order.

22. If segment $\overline{ED}$ is extended, it forms a transversal to the parallel lines ℓ and m. So this makes angle 1 and the angle 1' marked below alternate interior angles and thus congruent. If segment $\overline{EF}$ is extended, it forms a transversal to the parallel lines ℓ and m. So this makes angle 3 and the angle 3' marked below alternate interior angles and thus congruent. Since taken together the angles 1', 2 and 3' form a straight line or angle (line ℓ), their sum is 180°. Hence the sum of angle 1, angle 2 and angle 3 is 180°.

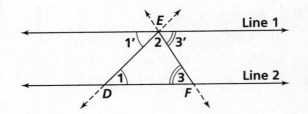

Extensions

23. One way to reason is as follows:

Step 1. $\triangle ADE \cong \triangle DAB$ by Side-Angle-Side

Step 2. $\angle EAD \cong \angle BDA$ (from congruent triangles in step 1)

Step 3. $\angle BAC \cong \angle EDC$. (We are given that $\angle BAD \cong \angle EDA$, and subtracting the congruent angles from step 2 yields $\angle BAC \cong \angle EDC$)

Step 4. $\angle ABD \cong \angle DEA$ (from congruent triangles in step 1)

Step 5. Angle ($\angle ABD \cong \angle DEA$ step 4), Side ($AB \cong ED$, given), Angle ($\angle BAC \cong \angle EDC$, step 3) shows that $\triangle ABC \cong \triangle DEC$.

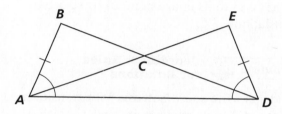

24. **Step 1.** Since C is at the center of the circle, lines $\overline{AC}$, $\overline{DC}$, $\overline{EC}$, and $\overline{BC}$ are all congruent.

Step 2. $\angle ACB \cong \angle DCE$ (opposite angles of intersecting lines)

Step 3. Side-Angle-Side shows that $\triangle ABC \cong \triangle DEC$

25. Students might reason by using symmetry as follows: The four triangles formed when the diagonals are drawn are all congruent since the diagonals of a rhombus lie on the lines of symmetry for the figure. So since all four triangles ($\triangle AED$, $\triangle AEB$, $\triangle CED$, $\triangle CEB$) are congruent $\angle AEB$, $\angle AED$, $\angle CED$, and $\angle CEB$ are all congruent. Thus these angles, all must be 90° since they are four angles surrounding a single point E. So diagonals $\overline{AC}$ and $\overline{BD}$ are perpendicular. Or students might reason by using facts about angles formed when a transversal cuts parallel lines. This ensures that the triangles are 30-60-90, with the 90 degree angles at the intersection point of the diagonals.

Possible Answers to Mathematical Reflections

1. a. Two triangles are congruent if one can be moved around to fit exactly on top of the other. Corresponding angles in the two figures have the same measure. Corresponding sides have the same length. Everything is the same except possibly where they are and which direction they are facing.

b. Two triangles are similar if all corresponding angles have the same measure and there is a scale factor for which all sides of one of the triangles can be multiplied by to get the lengths of the corresponding sides of the other triangle.

c. Yes; for example two right triangles with sides 3, 4, 5 and 6, 8, 10 are similar since they have a scale factor of 2. But they are not congruent.

d. No; If two triangles are congruent, all the angles are congruent and the scale factor is 1. So two congruent triangles will always be similar.

2. Possible answer: Since the isosceles triangle shown below has reflection symmetry in $\overline{AD}$, if we are given the sides and angle below we can find the measures of the other angles and sides.

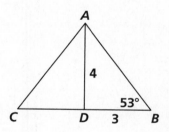

$\angle C$ and $\angle B$ are congruent so they have degree measures of 53°.
$\angle BAC$ must be $180 - 2(53) = 74°$.
$\angle ADC = \angle ADB = 90°$ and thus $\angle CAD$ and $\angle BAD$ each have a measure of 37°. Since segment $\overline{BD}$ is 3 and there is reflection symmetry, $\overline{CD}$ is also 3 units. So by the Pythagorean Theorem we get that segment $\overline{AB}$ is 5 and by symmetry $\overline{AC}$ is also 5.

Mathematical and Problem-Solving Goals

- Use coordinates to write directions for drawing figures composed of line segments

- Analyze the vertices of a figure in the coordinate plane and its image under a size and shape preserving transformation and specify the coordinates of the original and the image

- Specify coordinate rules for reflections in the x-axis, the y-axis, and the line $y = x$

- Recognize that a transformation of the form $(x, y) \rightarrow (x + a, y + b)$ is a translation of point (x, y) a units in the x direction and b units in the y direction

- Specify coordinate rules for rotations of 90°, 180°, 270°, and 360°

- Specify coordinate rules for combinations of transformations and find single, equivalent transformations if possible

Mathematics Background

For background on symmetry transformations, see pages 6–9

Summary of Problems

Problem 5.1 Coordinate Rules for Reflections

Students write coordinate rules for transforming a point (x, y) to its image point using selected reflections. The explorations are set in the context of writing computer instructions for drawing line segments, which focuses attention on what happens to the coordinates of a point under the desired transformation.

Problem 5.2 Coordinate Rules for Translations

Students write coordinate rules for transforming a point (x, y) to its image point using selected translations.

Problem 5.3 Coordinate Rules for Rotations

Students write coordinate rules for transforming a point (x, y) to its image point under selected rotations.

Problem 5.4 Coordinate Rules for Combinations of Transformations

Here students get a taste of what is involved in specifying a single transformation that produces the same result as one transformation followed by another. Using coordinate rules can help in keeping track of changes to the location of points.

	Suggested Pacing	Materials for Students	Materials for Teachers	ACE Assignments
All	$4\frac{1}{2}$ days	Student notebooks, tracing paper (or lightweight plain paper), grid paper, rulers, mirrors, transparent reflection tools, angle rulers or protractors (1 per group)	Blank transparency and transparency markers (optional), overhead graphing calculator (optional)	
5.1	1 day	Labsheets 5.1A, 5.1B, 5ACE 1–3	Transparencies 5.1A–C	1–3, 19, 25
5.2	1 day	Labsheets 5.2A–C	Transparencies 5.2A, 5.2B	4, 20, 21
5.3	1 day	Labsheets 5.3, 5ACE 5–14	Transparencies 5.3A, 5.3B	5–14, 22, 23, 26–28
5.4	1 day	Labsheets 5.4, 5ACE 15, 5ACE 23	Transparency 5.4	15–18, 24
MR	$\frac{1}{2}$ day			

5.1 Coordinate Rules for Reflections

Goals

- Use coordinates to write directions for drawing figures composed of line segments

- Analyze the vertices of a figure in the coordinate plane and its image under a size and shape preserving transformation and specify the coordinates of the original and the image

- Specify coordinate rules for reflections in the x-axis, the y-axis, and the line $y = x$

This problem introduces students to coordinate rules for reflections in the exploration of some simple cases.

Launch 5.1

Set the scene for the unit by looking with students at the character on the first page. The character is like characters students know from computer animations. This investigation will be an introduction to simple ways in which mathematics is used in the creation and movement of characters in animated movies and games.

Demonstrate the idea of making designs by specifying the endpoints of line segments. Use the example in the student edition, which is reproduced on Transparency 5.1 A, or make one of your own. The drawing instructions given here are generic, but they are much like those used in some graphing calculators and, though hidden from the user's view, in many computer drawing programs.

Draw: Line [(0, –2) , (0, 3)]
      Line [(0, 3) , (1, 2)]
      Line [(1, 2) , (0, 1)]

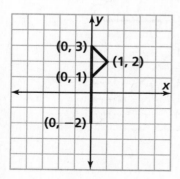

Verify that students see the relationship between the commands and the drawing the commands produce.

Help the class begin to analyze such figures by locating the points that are useful for determining what happens to the figure under a transformation. Four points, for example, essentially determine the flag shown above. Explain that directions are given to draw line segments between pairs of these points; the figure can be reproduced by another human being or by a computer.

Suggested Questions

- *Is there a different set of commands that would make the same flag?*

- *What commands would make a square centered at the origin?*

- *What commands would make a non-square rectangle?*

Have students share the commands they write. Two other sets of commands that would make the same flag are the following:

A. Draw:

  Line [(0, 3), (1, 2)]

  Line [(1, 2), (0, 1)]

  Line [(0, 1), (0, −2)]

  Line [(0, −2), (0, 3)]

B. Draw:

  Line [(0, 1), (0, 3)]

  Line [(0, 3), (1, 2)]

  Line [(1, 2), (0, 1)]

  Line [(0, 1), (0, −2)]

If directions are given to communicate what happens to these points under a desired transformation, the image of the figure can be drawn.

If we look closely at how these endpoints are transformed, it might help us to come up with a rule for drawing a figure under a particular transformation.

Suggested Question

- *What would be the coordinates of the flag if you reflected it over the y-axis?* [The points on the y-axis do not change. But the image point for $(1, 2)$ is $(−1, 2)$.]

Distribute copies of Labsheets 5.1A and 5.1B or grid paper to the groups, and have grid paper and tracing paper available for students to use during the exploration.

Assign the problem to be done in groups of two to four students.

Explore 5.1

For Question A, to write the new set of commands, students should draw and analyze the reflection image called for, focusing on the significant points in the image. They should realize that these are the same points that are significant in the original. For Question A, part (4), students may need assistance with drawing the line $y = x$.

Suggested Questions

- *Which of the points on the flag do not change? Which do?* [Only the point $(5, 3)$ changes. Its image point is $(3, 5)$.]

For Questions B, C, D, and E if students are having difficulty, focus their attention on the pairs of coordinates between the originals and the images. Have them organize their work so that it is easy to observe patterns in how the coordinates of the vertices change under reflection over different lines.

Going Further

Write directions for a reflection in the line $y = 3$ and for the line $x = -5$.
[For line $y = 3$, $(x, y) \rightarrow (x, -y + 6)$; for line $x = -5$, $(x, y) \rightarrow (-x - 10, y)$]

Summarize 5.1

Give students a chance to talk about what they observed in each subpart of Question A of the problem and to describe any patterns they see in what happens to the coordinate pairs under each of the targeted reflections—reflection over the x-axis, the y-axis, and the line $y = x$. Call on particular students you observed or on others to share their sets of commands for each part.

For Questions B, C, D, and E, ask students to share specific patterns they observed in their answers. These parts of the problem give students a chance to look at reflections in the y-axis, the x-axis, and the line $y = x$ in a different context. Here the focus is on points and their images rather than figures. The point to make here is that a reflection transforms every point in the plane

except those on the line of reflection. We focus on points that are of interest to us, but every point has an image under the reflection.

Check for Understanding

- *Draw the image of the flag in Question A under a reflection in:*

  1. $y = -x$

  2. $x = 2$

  3. $y = -2$.

Answers:

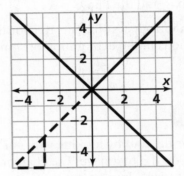

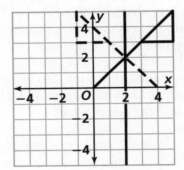

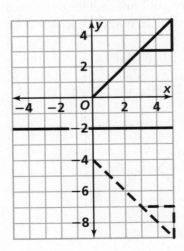

5.1 Coordinate Rules for Reflections

Mathematical Goals

- Use coordinates to write directions for drawing figures composed of line segments

- Analyze the vertices of a figure in the coordinate plane and its image under a size and shape preserving transformation and specify the coordinates of the original and the image

- Specify coordinate rules for reflections in the x-axis, the y-axis, and the line $y = x$

Launch

Use the example in the student edition to demonstrate making designs by specifying endpoints of line segments, which is reproduced on Transparency 5.1A.

Discuss the questions in the Getting Ready

- *Is there a different set of commands that would make the same flag? What commands would make a square centered at the origin? What commands would make a non-square rectangle?*

Have students share the commands they write.

- *What would be the coordinates of the flag if you reflected it in the y-axis?*

Distribute copies of Labsheet 5.1A or grid paper to the groups, and have grid paper and tracing paper available for students to use during the exploration.

Students can work in groups of two to four students.

Materials

- Transparency 5.1A–C
- Grid paper
- Mirrors or transparent reflecting tools
- Rulers, angle rulers, or protractors
- Tracing paper

Explore

For Question A, to write the new set of commands, students should draw and analyze the reflection image called for, focusing on the significant points in the image. They should realize that these are the same points that are significant in the original. For Question A, part (4), students may need assistance with drawing the line $y = x$. Ask:

- *Which of the points on the flag do not change? Which do?*

For Questions B, C, D, and E, if students are having difficulty, have them organize their work so that it is easy to observe patterns in how the coordinates of the vertices change under reflection over different lines.

See the extended Explore for a Going Further.

Materials

- Labsheet 5.1A and B
- Labsheet 5ACE 1–3

Discuss each of the subparts of Questions A–E and have students describe any patterns they see in coordinate pairs for reflection in the *y*-axis, the *x*-axis, and the line $y = x$.

See the extended Summarize for a Check for Understanding.

Materials
• Student notebooks

Vocabulary
• coordinate rules

ACE Assignment Guide for Problem 5.1

Core ACE 1–3
Other ACE *Connections* 19; *Extensions* 25;
unassigned choices from previous problems
Labsheet 5ACE Exercises 1–3 is provided if
Exercises 1–3 are assigned

Adapted For suggestions about adapting ACE
exercises, see the CMP *Special Needs Handbook.*
Assignment Guide for Problem 5.1

Answers to Problem 5.1

A. 1. One possibility:
Line $[(0, 0), (5, 5)]$
Line $[(5, 5), (5, 3)]$
Line $[(5, 3), (3, 3)]$

2. One possibility:
Line $[(0, 0), (-5, 5)]$
Line $[(-5, 5), (-5, 3)]$
Line $[(-5, 3), (-3, 3)]$
The rule is $(x, y) \rightarrow (-x, y)$
(**Note:** Students may describe this in
words.) Only (0,0) is unchanged.

3. One possibility:
Line $[(0, 0), (5, -5)]$
Line $[(5, -5), (5, -3)]$
Line $[(5, -3), (3, -3)]$
The rule is $(x, y) \rightarrow (x, -y)$
Only (0,0) is unchanged.

4. One possibility:
Line $[(0, 0), (5, 5)]$
Line $[(5, 5), (3, 5)]$
Line $[(3, 5), (3, 3)]$
The rule is $(x, y) \rightarrow (y, x)$
All points remain unchanged except (5,3),
which becomes (3,5).

B. $A\ (-3, 3)$
$B\ (-2, 4)$
$C\ (3, 3)$
$D\ (1, 2)$
$E\ (-4, -1)$
$F\ (-2, -4)$
$G\ (2, -2)$
$H\ (3, -4)$

C. 1. $A'\ (3, 3)$
$B'\ (2, 4)$
$C'\ (-3, 3)$
$D'\ (-1, 2)$
$E'\ (4, -1)$
$F'\ (2, -4)$
$G'\ (-2, -2)$
$H'\ (-3, -4)$

2. $(x, y) \rightarrow (-x, y)$

D. 1. $A''\ (-3, -3)$
$B''\ (-2, -4)$
$C''\ (3, -3)$
$D''\ (1, -2)$
$E''\ (-4, 1)$
$F''\ (-2, 4)$
$G''\ (2, 2)$
$H''\ (3, 4)$

2. $(x, y) \rightarrow (x, -y)$

E. 1. $A'''\ (3, -3)$
$B'''\ (4, -2)$
$C'''\ (3, 3)$
$D'''\ (2, 1)$
$E'''\ (-1, -4)$
$F'''\ (-4, -2)$
$G'''\ (-2, 2)$
$H'''\ (-4, 3)$

2. $(x, y) \rightarrow (y, x)$

Goals

- Specify coordinate rules for translations in the direction of the *x*-axis, the *y*-axis, and the line $y = x$

- Recognize that a transformation of the form $(x, y) \rightarrow (x + a, y + b)$ is a translation of point (x, y) *a* units in the *x* direction and *b* units in the *y* direction

In this problem, students examine pairs of points and images for various translations. The objective is for students to look for regular features of algebraic representations of translations so that they can both produce rules for translations and interpret such rules. Coordinate rules for translations are important throughout mathematics; developing informal knowledge through experience gives students valuable time to build their intuitive understanding.

The context is making designs with translation symmetry. Students have to *read* the magnitude and the direction from the images of the flags under different translations. Have grid paper available for students to make the patterns. Stress that students should be looking for patterns in what happens under the translations.

Some students may be ready to express the relationships in Questions A and B by writing coordinates that include a variable that represents the length of the translation; others will describe the relationships in words. Question C specifically asks for a rule, so you may wait until that part to ask students to capture their ideas in rules that use variables to represent the *x* and *y* values of a general point and its image point.

Launch 5.2

Direct students' attention to the two designs shown in parts A and B.

Suggested Questions

- *What type of symmetry do you see in these designs?* (translation symmetry)

- *How can you tell that each design exhibits translation symmetry?*

- *In this problem, you will look for patterns that relate each flag to the flag next to it. As you work, ask yourself whether there is a rule that relates a point to its translated image for a given translation.*

Have students work in pairs on the problem.

Explore 5.2

If students are having difficulty, focus their attention on the pairs of coordinates between the original and the first image. Have them organize their work so that it is easy to observe patterns in how the coordinates of the vertices change under the translation.

In Question C, students get a chance to experiment with translations where the possible directions of translation are specified, but the magnitude (distance) for the translations are not. As students work on this part, if a group is struggling, ask:

Suggested Questions

- *When you translate a figure along the line $y = x$, how is the change in the x-coordinate related to the change in the y-coordinate?* (When the *x*-coordinate increases by 1, the *y*-coordinate increases by 1.)

- *What is the slope of the line $y = x$?* (1)

- *How does the slope of the line relate to translating a figure along that line?* (The slope tells us that the *y*-coordinate would change by 1 whenever the *x*-coordinate changes by 1.)

Summarize 5.2

Call on students to share their answers for each part of the problem.

Suggested Questions

- *Give me a few rules showing what might happen to a point (x, y) under a translation parallel to the x-axis.* [Students might suggest such rules as $(x, y) \rightarrow (x + 2, y)$, $(x, y) \rightarrow (x - 4, y)$, and $(x, y) \rightarrow (x + 0.5, y)$.]

- *What do the rules for translations parallel to the x-axis have in common?* (The rules all add or subtract a number from the *x*-coordinate, but leave the *y*-coordinate alone.)

- *Can you write a "super rule" to handle all of these cases?* (Help students to see that a general rule is $(x, y) \rightarrow (x + a, y)$, where *a* gives the length and direction of the change parallel to the *x*-axis. If *a* is positive, the slide is to the right. If *a* is negative, the slide is to the left.)

- *Now give me a few rules showing what might happen to a point (x, y) under a translation parallel to the y-axis.* (Students might suggest such rules as $(x, y) \rightarrow (x, y + 1)$, $(x, y) \rightarrow (x, y - 4)$, and $(x, y) \rightarrow (x, y + 0.5)$.)

- *What do the rules for translations parallel to the y-axis have in common?* [These rules are of the form $(x, y) \rightarrow (x, y + a)$, where *a* gives the length and direction of the change parallel to the *y*-axis.]

- *Now give me a few rules showing what might happen to a point (x, y) under a translation parallel to the line y = x.* (Students might suggest such rules as $(x, y) \rightarrow (x + 1, y + 1)$, $(x, y) \rightarrow (x - 4, y - 4)$, and $(x, y) \rightarrow (x + 0.5, x + 0.5)$.)

- *What do the rules for translations parallel to the line y = x have in common?* [These rules are of the form $(x, y) \rightarrow (x + a, y + a)$, where *a* gives the length and direction of the change in the *x* direction, which is identical to the change in the *y* direction.]

- *If you are given a rule, how can you recognize whether it describes a translation?* (It would show that something is added to or subtracted from *x* or *y* or both.)

- *What about the rule (x, y) → (2x, y)? Does it describe a translation?* (No, the figure seems to be stretched.)

You might sketch an example of a figure being transformed according to this rule. The square shown below increases in size in the *x* direction, which means this rule does not describe a translation.

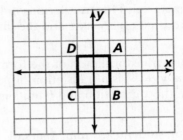

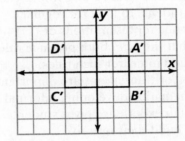

Check for Understanding

- *Which of the following rules represent translations?*

  1. $(x, y) \rightarrow (x, y - 10)$
  2. $(x, y) \rightarrow (\frac{1}{2}x, y + \frac{1}{2})$
  3. $(x, y) \rightarrow (-2 + x, y)$
  4. $(x, y) \rightarrow (x + 3, y - 5)$

  (Answer: 1, 3, and 4 represent translations. Number 2 does not.)

Mathematical Goals

- Specify coordinate rules for translations in the direction of the x-axis, the y-axis, and the line $y = x$

- Recognize that a transformation of the form $(x, y) \rightarrow (x + a, y + b)$ is a translation of point (x, y) a units in the x direction and b units in the y direction

Launch

Direct students' attention to the two designs shown in Questions A and B.

- *What type of symmetry do you see in these designs?*

- *How can you tell that each design exhibits translation symmetry?*

- *In this problem, you will look for patterns that relate each flag to the flag next to it. As you work, ask yourself whether there is a rule that relates a point to its translated image for a given translation.*

Have students work in pairs on the problem.

Materials
- Transparency 5.2A, B
- Grid paper
- Mirrors or transparent reflecting tools
- Rulers, angle rulers, or protractors
- Tracing paper

Explore

If students are struggling with Question C, ask

- *When you translate a figure along the line $y = x$, how is the change in the x-coordinate related to the change in the y-coordinate?*

- *What is the slope of the line $y = x$?*

- *How does the slope of the line relate to translating a figure along that line?*

Materials
- Labsheets 5.3A, B, and C

Summarize

- *What might happen to a point (x, y) under a translation parallel to the x-axis?*

- *What do all rules for translations parallel to the x-axis have in common?*

- *What might happen to a point (x, y) under a translation parallel to the y-axis?*

- *What do all rules for translations parallel to the y-axis have in common?*

- *What might happen to a point (x, y) under a translation parallel to the line $y = x$?*

- *What do the rules for translations parallel to the line $y = x$ have in common?*

- *If you are given a rule, how can you recognize whether it describes a translation?*

- *Does the rule $(x, y) \rightarrow (2x, y)$ describe a translation?*

See the extended Summarize for a Check for Understanding.

Materials
- Student notebooks

ACE Assignment Guide for Problem 5.2

Core 4, 20, 21

Adapted For suggestions about adapting ACE exercises, see the CMP *Special Needs Handbook*.

Answers to Problem 5.2

A. 1. flag 2–Draw:
Line [(−3, −4), (−3, 2)]
Line [(−3, 2), (−2, 1)]
Line [(−2, 1), (−3, 0)]

flag 3–Draw:
Line [(−1, −4), (−1, 2)]
Line [(−1, 2), (0, 1)]
Line [(0, 1), (−1, 0)]

flag 4–Draw:
Line [(1, −4), (1, 2)]
Line [(1, 2), (2, 1)]
Line [(2, 1), (1, 0)]

flag 5–Draw:
Line [(3, −4), (3, 2)]
Line [(3, 2), (4, 1)]
Line [(4, 1), (3, 0)]

2. To find the coordinates of the flag to the right of a given flag, add 2 to each x-coordinate and keep the y-coordinates the same.

3. To find the coordinates of the flag to the left of a given flag, subtract 2 from each x-coordinate and keep the y-coordinates the same.

B. 1. flag 1–Draw:
Line [(−4, −4), (−4, 0)]
Line [(−4, 0), (−3, −1)]
Line [(−3, −1), (−4, −2)]

flag 2–Draw:
Line [(−2, −3), (−2, 1)]
Line [(−2, 1), (−1, 0)]
Line [(−1, 0), (−2, −1)]

flag 3–Draw:
Line [(0, −2), (0, 2)]
Line [(0, 2), (1, 1)]
Line [(1, 1), (0, 0)]

flag 4–Draw:
Line [(2, −1), (2, 3)]
Line [(2, 3), (3, 2)]
Line [(3, 2), (2, 1)]

flag 5–Draw:
Line [(4, 0), (4, 4)]
Line [(4, 4), (5, 3)]
Line [(5, 3), (4, 2)]

2. To find the coordinates of the flag to the right of a given flag, add 2 to each x-coordinate and 1 to each y-coordinate.

3. To find the coordinates of the flag to the left of a given flag, subtract 2 from each x-coordinate and 1 from each y-coordinate.

C. 1. For sliding the figure along a line parallel to the x-axis: The x-coordinate of the figure to the right of a given figure is x plus the length of the translation; the y-coordinate does not change.
For sliding the figure along a line parallel to the y-axis: The x-coordinate of the figure above a given figure does not change; the y-coordinate is y plus the length of the translation.
For sliding the figure along a line parallel to the line $y = x$: The same values are added to both x and y coordinates. (**Note:** The distance of the translation can be found from these changes by using the Pythagorean Theorem.)

2. a. $(x, y) \rightarrow (x + b, y)$
  b. $(x, y) \rightarrow (x, y + b)$
  c. $(x, y) \rightarrow (x + b, y + b)$

D. 1. A translation that moves the point 2 to the right and 3 down.

2. This is a stretch in the x direction, not a translation.

3. This moves the figure 1 unit in the x-direction, but stretches it in the y-direction. It is not a translation.

4. This is a translation left 2 in the x direction and up 1 in the y direction.

5. Answered above.

Coordinate Rules for Rotations

Goal

- Specify coordinate rules for rotations of 90°, 180°, 270°, and 360°

This problem follows the format of the two earlier problems, but this time the transformation is rotation. Only rotations that are 90° or multiples of 90° are considered with the origin as the center of rotation so that students can easily observe what happens to the coordinates. In high school, students in transformational geometry courses will learn to specify other turns algebraically.

Launch 5.3

Since this problem is similar to Problems 5.1 and 5.2, students should be able to anticipate the goal of the exploration. You might introduce the activity by making two copies of the triangle in the problem on transparencies and rotating one on top of the other about the origin to demonstrate a 90° rotation, a 180° rotation, a 270° rotation, and a 360° rotation. Remind students that rotations in this unit are done in a counterclockwise direction.

Suggested Questions

- *How do the coordinates of a point on flag 1 compare to their image points under a 90° rotation? What about the points on flags 2, 3, and 4? Try some points to see. Record your results.*

- *Do you see a pattern in the way the coordinates of a point change that would give a rule for how the coordinates for any point change under a 90° rotation?*

Let students work in pairs on the problem. Have grid paper and tracing paper available for use during the exploration.

Explore 5.3

As you circulate, listen for ideas that you would like shared in the summary. Also listen for ideas with which students are having trouble, and make a note to emphasize these in the summary.

Summarize 5.3

As students share their answers to Question A, help the class to organize the data into a table as called for in Question B. With this evidence displayed, discussion of Question B, part (2) and part (3) can help students make the leap to generalizing the result of a specific rotation.

Suggested Questions

- *Let's look carefully at each rotation, 90°, 180°, 270°, and 360°. For 90°, look at the points after each transformation. How do the original points relate to the coordinates of the image points?* (The *x*- and *y*-coordinates change places and then the sign of *x* changes.)

Help the class to see why this makes sense.

- *If you were to rotate a grid 90°, what would happen to the x-axis?* (It would become the *y*-axis.)

- *What would happen to the y-axis?* (It would become the *x*-axis, but the positive end of the *y*-axis is now negative and the negative end is positive.)

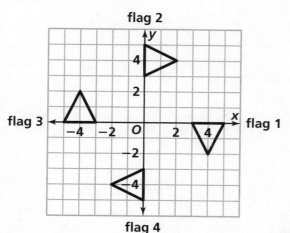

flag 2

flag 3

flag 1

flag 4

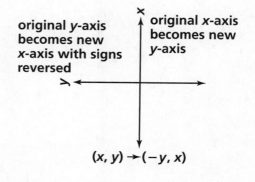

original *y*-axis becomes new *x*-axis with signs reversed

original *x*-axis becomes new *y*-axis

$(x, y) \rightarrow (-y, x)$

- *What about a 180° turn?* (The signs of the coordinates are changed.)

Let's rotate the grid for a 180° turn.

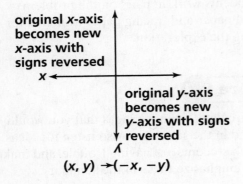

original *x*-axis becomes new *x*-axis with signs reversed

original *y*-axis becomes new *y*-axis with signs reversed

$(x, y) \rightarrow (-x, -y)$

- *What about a 270° turn?* (The coordinates change places, and then the sign of *y* changes.)

Let's track the axes to see whether this makes sense.

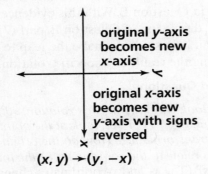

original *y*-axis becomes new *x*-axis

original *x*-axis becomes new *y*-axis with signs reversed

$(x, y) \rightarrow (y, -x)$

5.3 Coordinate Rules for Rotations

Mathematical Goal

- Specify coordinate rules for rotations of 90°, 180°, 270°, and 360°

Launch

Introduce the activity by making two copies of the triangle in the problem on transparencies and rotating one on top of the other about the origin to demonstrate a 90° rotation, a 180° rotation, a 270° rotation, and a 360° rotation. Remind students that rotations in this unit are done in a counterclockwise direction. Read through the problem with students as you show the rotations to emphasize that their goal is to observe what happens to the vertices of the triangle under the transformation.

Let students work in pairs on the problem.

Materials
- Transparency 5.1A–C
- Grid paper
- Mirrors or transparent reflecting tools
- Rulers, angle rulers, or protractors
- Tracing paper

Explore

As you circulate, listen for ideas that you would like shared in the summary. Also listen for ideas with which students are having trouble, and make a note to emphasize these in the summary.

Materials
- Labsheet 5.3
- Labsheets 5ACE 5–14 and 5ACE Exercise 23

Summarize

As students share their answers to Question A, help the class organize the data into a table for in Question B. With this evidence displayed, discussion of Questions B, part (2) and part (3) can help students make the leap to generalizing the result of a specific rotation. Ask:

- *Let's look carefully at each rotation, 90°, 180°, 270°, and 360°. For 90°, look at the points after each transformation. How do the coordinates of the image points relate to the coordinates of the original points?*
- *If you were to rotate a grid 90°, what would happen to the x-axis?*
- *What would happen to the y-axis?*
- *What about a 180° turn?*
- *What about a 270° turn?*
- *Let's track the axes to see whether this makes sense.*

Materials
- Student notebooks

ACE Assignment Guide
for Problem 5.3

Core 5–14, 22
Other *Connections* 23; *Extensions* 26–28;
unassigned choices from previous problems

Labsheet 5ACE Exercises 5–14 and 5ACE
Exercise 23 are provided if Exercises 5–14 and 23
are assigned

Adapted For suggestions about adapting ACE
exercises, see the CMP *Special Needs Handbook.*

Answers to Problem 5.3

A. 1. Draw:
Line [(1, 4), (4, 2)]
Line [(4, 2), (2, 0)]
Line [(2, 0), (1, 4)]

2. a. Draw:
Line [(−4, 1), (−2, 4)]
Line [(−2, 4), (0, 2)]
Line [(0, 2), (−4, 1)]

b. Draw:
Line [(−1, −4), (−4, −2)]
Line [(−4, −2), (−2, 0)]
Line [(−2, 0), (−1, −4)]

c. Draw:
Line [(4, −1), (2, −4)]
Line [(2, −4), (0, −2)]
Line [(0, −2), (4, −1)]

d. Draw:
Line [(1, 4), (4, 2)]
Line [(4, 2), (2, 0)]
Line [(2, 0), (1, 4)]

B. 1. Figure 1

2. Under a 90° rotation, the
x- and y-coordinates exchange places, and
then the sign of the new x-coordinate is
reversed. Under a 180° rotation, the signs of
the x- and y-coordinates are reversed.
Under a 270° rotation, the
x- and y-coordinates exchange places, and
then the sign of the new y-coordinate is
reversed. Under a 360° rotation, the
x- and y-coordinates are unchanged.

3. a. 90° rotation: $(x, y) \rightarrow (-y, x)$

b. 180° rotation: $(x, y) \rightarrow (-x, -y)$

c. 270° rotation: $(x, y) \rightarrow (y, -x)$

d. 360° rotation: $(x, y) \rightarrow (x, y)$

Figure 1

Starting Point	90° Rotation	180° Rotation	270° Rotation	360° Rotation
A (1, 4)	(−4, 1)	(−1, −4)	(4, −1)	(1, 4)
B (4, 2)	(−2, 4)	(−4, −2)	(2, −4)	(4, 2)
C (2, 0)	(0, 2)	(−2, 0)	(0, −2)	(2, 0)

Coordinate Rules for Transformation Combinations

Goal

- Specify coordinate rules for combinations of transformations and find single, equivalent transformations if possible

One of the payoffs for using coordinate forms of transformations is to be able to do "arithmetic" with transformation performed in sequence to seek a single transformation that will accomplish the same final result. Of course, you can actually perform the transformations in sequence, using the image just drawn as the starting image for the next transformation. However, this can be difficult and still leaves the problem of finding, if there exists one, a single transformation that will accomplish the same result. You can think of this as a kind of *adding transformations together*. Natural questions to ask are is such an operation commutative. If the transformations are performed in a different order, will the result be the same? These are the questions behind this investigation.

This problem only touches on combining transformations. This is just enough to give students a glimmer of the power of coordinate representations. As students proceed in their study of geometry in high school and beyond, they should meet these ideas again and study them in a deeper way. The intent here is to suggest reasons why coordinate representations are powerful, but not to work to a level of proficiency in this area. Later students will see that composing two translations is like adding two vectors. The graphic below shows the arrows (1 and 2) representing two translations performed in sequence and the arrow of the combination (3).

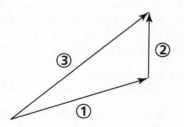

Launch 5.4

Start by reviewing what students have done so far to get them ready.

Suggested Questions

- *Here are some transformations given in coordinate form. For each one, tell what the transformation is and describe in words how the original position of the shape and the image under the transformation are related.*

  1. $(x, y) \rightarrow (-x, y)$ 2. $(x, y) \rightarrow (-y, x)$
  3. $(x, y) \rightarrow (x - 4, y + 5)$
  [(1) A reflection in the y-axis; (2) a 90° counterclockwise rotation; (3) a translation to the left 4 and up 5.]

- *What would happen if you started with a figure and performed a reflection in the y-axis on the original and another reflection in the y-axis on the image?* (You end up where you start.)

- *What if you do a translation of 4 to the left and 5 up and then do the same thing with the image? Where is a point on the original figure in the final image?* (The final image point will be 8 units to the left and 10 up.)

- *As you work on this problem 5.4, this is the kind of thinking that you are asked to do. In addition, you are asked to find a single transformation that will accomplish what a combination of transformations will accomplish.*

- *What would you write for the combination of two reflections in the y-axis?* [$(x, y) \rightarrow (x, y)$]

- *Could you show what I just asked in coordinate form?* [Yes. $(x, y) \rightarrow (-x, y) \rightarrow (- -x, y)$ which is (x, y), the first arrow represents the first reflection in y-axis and the second arrow is the second reflection in the y-axis.]

- *These are the kinds of things you are asked to do in the problem.*

Let students work in small groups on this problem.

Encourage students who are struggling to describe in words what moves the figures make and then try to symbolize their words. Also, remind them that they can actually carry out the transformations and examine the result to help write the rule.

Suggested Questions

- *Just think about these in your mind.*

- *What would happen to a figure under a translation followed by another translation? Except for location, would it look different in the plane?* (No. It would still be oriented the same.)

- *What would happen to a figure under a reflection followed by another reflection? Except for location, would it look different in the plane?* (Sometimes it would look different. For example, for a reflection in the line $x = 3$ followed by a reflection in the line $x = 7$ the figure will be oriented the same. However after a reflection in the x-axis followed by a reflection in the y-axis, the figure will not be oriented in the same direction.)

- *What would happen to a figure under a rotation followed by another rotation? Except for location, would it look different in the plane?* (Yes. It would be turned unless the sum of the rotation angles is a multiple of 360°.)

- *Can you think of a rotation followed by another rotation that would give a final figure that looked the same?* (A 180° followed by another 180° around the same center would give the original figure back again.)

- *Try to picture in your mind what is happening, what is the coordinate representation for a 180° rotation followed by another 180° rotation?* $[(x, y) \rightarrow (-x, -y) \rightarrow (- -x, - -y) \rightarrow (x, y)]$

Summarize 5.4

Go over the parts with the students. First discuss Question A.

Suggested Questions

- *What are several different ways to move the basic shape in Question A from position 1 to position 2?* (Some possibilities are: You can translate on a diagonal from A to B. You can slide vertically until the segment with endpoint A is on the same grid line as the segment with endpoint B and then slide horizontally until A matches B. You can slide horizontally until A is directly under B and then slide vertically until A matches B.)

- *Show us with coordinate rules how to move the basic shape from 1 to 2.* [Some possibilities are: one translation $(x, y) \rightarrow (x + 4, y + 4)$; two translations with a move in the horizontal direction followed by a second move in the vertical direction $(x, y) \rightarrow (x + 4, y) \rightarrow (x + 4, y + 4)$; or two translations with a move in the vertical direction followed by a second move in the horizontal direction $(x, y) \rightarrow (x, y + 4) \rightarrow (x + 4, y + 4)]$

- *What is different about a move from position 1 to position 3?* (The only difference is that the magnitude of the slide in a horizontal direction is greater. The slide in the vertical direction is the same.)

- *What would the coordinate rule for part 2a look like?* $[(x, y) \rightarrow (x + a, y + a) \rightarrow \{(x + a) + c, (y + a)\}$ or $\{x + (a + c), y + a\}]$

- *What would the rule for part 2b look like?* $[(x, y) \rightarrow (x + c, y) \rightarrow \{(x + c) + a, (y + a)\}$ or $\{x + (c + a), y + a\}]$

- *How do the final results compare?* (They are the same. Yes, they should always be the same because the sum of the vertical moves and the sum of the horizontal moves will get you to the same final place regardless of the order in which they are done.)

For Question B you are dealing with a combination of two different kinds of transformations.

Suggested Questions

- *How can you to move the triangle shape from position 1 to position 2?* (Possible answers are a translation followed by a rotation or a rotation followed by a translation.)

- *What coordinate rule specifies a rotation of 180° around the origin?* $[(x, y) \rightarrow (-x, -y)]$

- *Who can tell us in words how to think about Question B, part (1b)?* (First you have to rotate the triangle. In the rotation of 180° the x value and the y value change their signs. Then for the translation in the line $y = x$, you add the same amount to each coordinate.)

- *What does this look like as coordinate rules?*
  $[(x, y) \rightarrow (-x, -y) \rightarrow (-x + a, -y + a)]$

- *In Question B, part (1c) the order of the transformation is reversed. First we do the translation from 1 to 2 and then the rotation around the origin. Do you get the same result?* (No)

- *How could we show using coordinate representations that these two combinations do not result in the same final transformation.*
  $[(x, y) \rightarrow (x + a, y + a) \rightarrow$
  $\{-(x + a), \{-(y + a)\}]$ (This is the same as $(-x - a, -y - a)$ but different from what we got when we did these in the other order. The final image does not match the triangle in position 2.)

- *Why did the second order not work out?* (The center of rotation is not the one that is needed to make the final move to match triangle 2. The center of the rotation that is needed is not the origin. It is the midpoint of the side of the triangle on the line $y = x$.)

5.4 Coordinate Rules for Combinations of Transformations

Mathematical Goal

- Specify coordinate rules for combinations of transformations and find single, equivalent transformations if possible

Launch

- *For each, tell what the transformation is and describe in words how the original position of the shape and the image under the transformation are related.*
    1. $(x, y) \rightarrow (-x, y)$
    2. $(x, y) \rightarrow (-y, x)$
    3. $(x, y) \rightarrow (x - 4, y + 5)$
- *What would happen if you started with a figure and performed a reflection over the y-axis on the original and another reflection over the y-axis on the image?*
- *What if you do a translation of 4 to the left and 5 up and then do the same thing with the image? Where is a point on the original figure in the final image?*
- *This is the kind of thinking that you are asked to do here. In addition, you are asked to find a single transformation that will that will get you to the same place as a combination of transformations.*

Let students work in small groups on this problem.

Materials
- Transparency 5.4
- Grid paper
- Mirrors or transparent reflecting tools
- Rulers, angle rulers, or protractors
- Tracing paper

Explore

- *Think about these in your mind.*
- *What would happen to a figure under a translation followed by another translation? Except for location, would it look different in the plane?*

Repeat for reflection and then rotation.

- *Try to picture in your mind what is happening, and then think about the coordinate representation.*

Materials
- Labsheet 5.4
- Labsheet 5.ACE 15

Summarize

- *Describe a way to move the basic shape in Question A from position 1 to position 2.*
- *What would the coordinate rule for Question A, part (2a) look like?*
- *What would the rule for Question B, part (2b) look like? How do the final results compare?*

Materials
- Student notebooks

continued on next page

For Question B ask them to:

- *Describe one way you thought about moving the shape to another position. Tell in words how to think about Question B. What does this look like as coordinate rules? In Question C the order of the transformation is reversed. Do you get the same result?*

- *Prove it using coordinate representations.*

- *Why did the second order not work out?*

ACE Assignment Guide for Problem 5.4

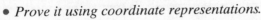

Differentiated Instruction
Solutions for All Learners

Core 15–17, 24
Other *Application* 18; unassigned choices from previous problems

Labsheets 5ACE Exercise 15 is provided if Exercise 15 is assigned

Adapted For suggestions about adapting Exercise 16 and other ACE exercises, see the CMP *Special Needs Handbook.*
Connecting to Prior Units 23: *Shapes and Designs*

Answers to Problem 5.4

A. 1. a. Some possibilities are: You can translate on a diagonal from *A* to *B*. You can slide vertically until *A* is on the same horizontal grid line as *B* and then slide horizontally until *A* matches *B*. You can slide horizontally until *A* is directly under *B* and then slide vertically until *A* matches *B*.

b. The only difference from Question A is that the magnitude of the slide in a horizontal direction is greater. The slide in the vertical direction is the same.

2. a. $(x, y) \rightarrow (x + 4, y + 4) \rightarrow [(x + 4) + 5, y + 4] = (x + 9, y + 4)$

b. $(x, y) \rightarrow (x + 5, y) \rightarrow \{(x + 5) + 4, y + 4\} = (x + 9, y + 4)$

c. They are the same. Yes, they should always be the same because the diagonal move and the horizontal move will get you to the same final place regardless of the order in which they are done. The coordinate rules indicate we are just adding real numbers in different orders.

B. 1. a. $[(x, y) \rightarrow (-x, -y)]$

b. $[(x, y) \rightarrow (-x, -y) \rightarrow (-x + a, -y + a)]$

c. No. You get $[(x, y) \rightarrow (x + a, y + a) \rightarrow \{-(x + a), \{-(y + a)\}\}]$. This is the same as $(-x - a, -y - a)$ but different from what we got when we did these in the other order. The final image does not match the triangle in position 2.

2. If we slide △1 first, and then rotate around the origin, the figure ends up in quadrant 3. If we want to end up in the position and orientation of △2, we would have to slide △1 first and then choose a different center of rotation. The center of the rotation that is needed is not the origin. It is the midpoint of the side of the triangle on the line $y = x$. The rule we have for the coordinates of the image of (x, y) under a rotation only works for a rotation around $(0, 0)$.

Investigation 5

ACE Assignment Choices

Differentiated Instruction
Solutions for All Learners

Problem 5.1

Core 1–3

Other *Connections* 19; *Extensions* 25; unassigned choices from previous problems

Problem 5.2

Core 4, 20, 21

Problem 5.3

Core 5–14, 22

Other *Connections* 23; *Extensions* 26–28; unassigned choices from previous problems

Problem 5.4

Core 15–17, 24

Other *Application* 18; unassigned choices from previous problems

Adapted For suggestions about adapting Exercise 16 and other ACE exercises, see the CMP *Special Needs Handbook*.

Connecting to Prior Units 23: *Shapes and Designs*;

Applications

1. **a.** Possible answer:
   Draw:
   Line [(1, −3), (1, 3)]
   Line [(1, 3), (4, 3)]
   Line [(4, 3), (4, 0)]
   Line [(4, 0), (2, 0)]
   Line [(2, 0), (4, −3)]

   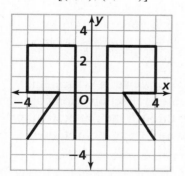

   b. Possible answer:
   Draw:
   Line [(−1, −3), (−1, 3)]
   Line [(−1, 3), (−4, 3)]
   Line [(−4, 3), (−4, 0)]
   Line [(−4, 0), (−2, 0)]
   Line [(−2, 0), (−4, −3)]

2. **a.** Possible answer:
   Draw:
   Line [(−4, −4), (0, 4)]
   Line [(0, 4), (4, −4)]
   Line [(−2, 0), (2, 0)]

   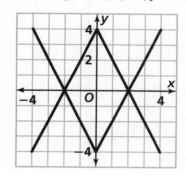

   b. Possible answer:
   Draw:
   Line [(−4, 4), (0, −4)]
   Line [(0, −4), (4, 4)]
   Line [(−2, 0), (2, 0)]

3. **a.** Possible answer:
   Draw:
   Line [(−1, 5), (−4, 5)]
   Line[(−4, 5), (−4, 1)]
   Line [(−4, 3), (−2, 3)]

   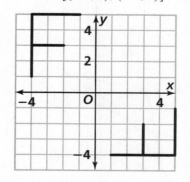

b. Possible answer:
Draw:
Line $[(5, -1), (5, -4)]$
Line $[(5, -4), (1, -4)]$
Line $[(3, -4), (3, -2)]$

4. a. Possible answer:

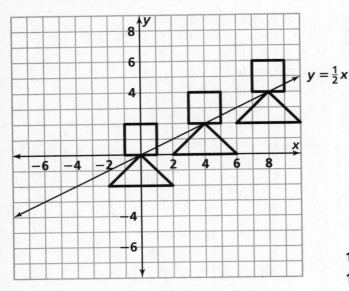

$y = \frac{1}{2}x$

b. The coordinates for the graphic above changed from $(x, y) \rightarrow (x + 4, y + 2)$. In general the coordinates change from $(x, y) \rightarrow (x + 2a, y + a)$ where a is a non-zero constant.

c. Possible translations along the line $y = \frac{1}{2}x$: $(x, y) \rightarrow (x + 3, y + 1) \rightarrow (x + 4, y + 2) \rightarrow (x + 5, y + 3)$ and so on.

5. $(-2, 5)$ **6.** $(0, 1)$

7. $(0, -2)$ **8.** $(-1, 2)$

9. $(4, -1)$ **10.** $(-2, 2)$

11. $(4, 3)$ **12.** $(-5, 5)$

13. $(-4, 2)$ **14.** $(4, 1)$

15. a. The image, polygon $A'B'C'D'$, is shown below.

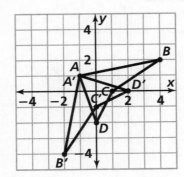

b. The image, polygon $A''B''C''D''$, is shown below.

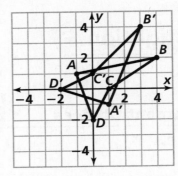

c. A rotation of 90° followed by a reflection over the x-axis takes point (x, y) to point $(-y, x)$ and then takes $(-y, x)$ to point $(-y, -x)$. A reflection over the x-axis followed by a rotation of 90° takes point (x, y) to point $(x, -y)$ and then takes point $(x, -y)$ to point (y, x). They are not the same, so order matters.

16. a 360° rotation about the origin

17. a reflection over the x-axis

18. Answers will vary. If students perform reflections over intersecting lines or rotations about the same center, they can find a single, equivalent rotation. If they perform reflections over parallel lines, they can find a single, equivalent translation. If they combine two translations, they can find a single, equivalent translation. If they combine a reflection and a translation, they can find a single, equivalent glide reflection. There are other combinations that students might try.

Connections

19. a. P and R, Q and S, S and Q

b. a 180° rotation about the midpoint of segment QS

c. sides: $\overline{PQ} \cong \overline{RS}$, $\overline{PS} \cong \overline{RQ}$, $\overline{QS} \cong \overline{SQ}$; angles: $\angle P \cong \angle R$, $\angle PQS \cong \angle RSQ$, $\angle PSQ \cong \angle RQS$

20. Reflection symmetry over a vertical line through the center; reflection symmetry over a horizontal line through the center; rotational symmetry with a 180° angle of rotation

21. reflection symmetries over the lines connecting opposite vertices of the hexagon; reflection symmetries over the lines connecting opposite midpoints of the sides of the hexagon; rotation symmetry with a 60° angle of rotation.

22. a. center at $(0, 0)$; 180° angle of rotation

b. Each coordinate of an image point is the opposite of the corresponding coordinate of the original point.

23. a. P goes to S, Q goes to R and R goes to Q.

b. Side $\overline{PQ} \cong \overline{RS}, \overline{PR} \cong \overline{QS}, \overline{RQ} \cong \overline{QR}$, $\angle RPQ \cong \angle QSR$, $\angle RQP \cong \angle QRS$ and $\angle PRQ \cong \angle RQS$

c. Vertex S has coordinates $(-x, -y)$ and Vertex R $(-r, -s)$

d. A parallelogram; we can use equal alternate interior angles to show opposite sides are parallel. Or we could say that $PQRS$ has rotation symmetry, which is only true for quadrilaterals that are parallelograms.

e. No, the resulting image is not the same.

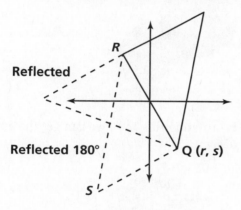

24. B

Extensions

25. One possible design is shown below. It was made by reflecting the original over the y-axis and then reflecting both the original and its image over the x-axis.

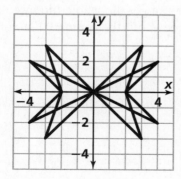

26. One possible design is shown below. It was made by rotating the original 90° about the origin, and then rotating the image 90° about the origin, and finally rotating the second image 90° about the origin.

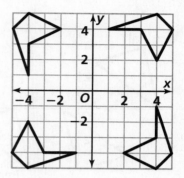

27. One possible design is shown below. One way to make the final design is to transform the original design; first, reflect the original "F" over the y-axis, and then reflect the original "F" and its image, over the x-axis. The first reflection produces a design with reflection symmetry over the y-axis, but no rotation symmetry. The second reflection ensures that the design has reflection symmetry over both the y-axis and the x-axis, and *also* rotation symmetry, 180°, around the origin. The result of combining a reflection transformation over the y-axis with a reflection transformation over the x-axis is *always* the same as a single rotation transformation of 180° around the origin.

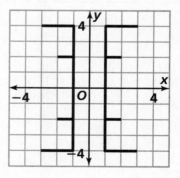

28. A 180° rotation about one point followed by a 180° rotation about a second point is equivalent to a translation parallel to the line connecting the two points. In each example given, the original polygon can be translated to match image 2.

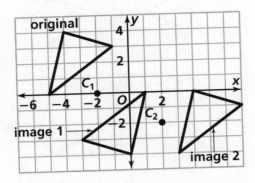

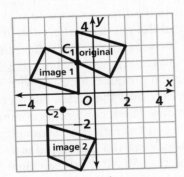

Possible Answers to Mathematical Reflections

1. $(-x, y)$
2. $(x, -y)$
3. (y, x)
4. $(-y, x)$
5. $(-x, -y)$
6. $(y, -x)$
7. (x, y)
8. $(x + 2, y - 4)$
9. $(x - 6, y - 2)$
10. $(x, y) \rightarrow (-y, x) \rightarrow (y, x)$

Answers to Looking Back and Looking Ahead

1. a. The pattern has translation symmetry. We can move the whole pattern horizontally 4.2 cm and have it look the same as before the move. The design has reflection symmetry with vertical lines of reflection through the centers of the suns and also through the centers of the stars. Because the stars do not have the same vertical spacing as the suns, the pattern does not have horizontal lines of reflection. The pattern has 180° rotational symmetry around the center of each star and each sun.

   b. 45°

2. a. The tile has 180° rotational symmetry. It has 2 lines of symmetry: horizontal and vertical.

   b. The smallest basic design element is:

By rotating this 180°, we can get the entire design:

We can get the whole tile by rotating this piece about the center, 90° at a time.

3. a.

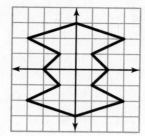

b.

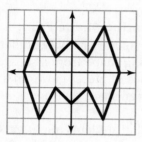

c.

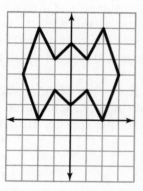

4. a. Three measures. You could make all three sides 6 cm and the triangle will be congruent to *ABC*. Alternatively, you could use two sixty degree angles and 6 cm side. Two sides and the angle between them would also work (e.g. side *AB*, angle *B* and side *BC*).

b. It is not true that ANY three measures will be sufficient. It would not be sufficient to use only the three angles. This would guarantee similarity, but not congruence.

5. a. Segments *PR* and *PQ* are congruent.

b. Angles *Q* and *R* are congruent.

c. Point *M* is the midpoint of segment *QR*.

d. ∠*RPM* and ∠*QPM* are congruent.

Triangles *RPM* and *QPM* are congruent because *k* is a line of symmetry. All of the pairs listed above are corresponding parts, and so must be congruent.

6. a. Possible answer: Cut out a picture of the figure and then cut that in half along the line. Show the person that when you flip one half over it looks exactly like the other half. Alternatively, you could connect corresponding points with segments and draw in the perpendicular bisector of these segments. This line will be the line of reflection.

b. Possible answer: Cut out a picture of the figure and rotate it to show the person that it looks the same after rotating it. Alternatively, find the center of rotation and show the person that corresponding points are at equal distances from the center and that for each pair, the angle between the lines connecting each point to the center is the same measure.

c. Possible answer: Cut out a portion of the design and move it to show that it can fall perfectly on top of another portion. Alternatively, measure the distance and angle between corresponding points to verify that these measures are the same for every pair of corresponding points.

7. Connect two corresponding points with a segment. Draw the line perpendicular to this segment, through its midpoint. Repeat with another pair of corresponding points. These two lines will meet at the center of rotation. The angle between the lines is the angle of rotation.

8. Connect any two corresponding points. Draw the line perpendicular to this segment, through its midpoint. This line is the line of reflection.

9. All three sides. Any two angles and any one side. Two sides and the angle between them.

10. All three angles. For most triangles, two sides and an angle NOT between them is insufficient to know that the two triangles are congruent.

Guide to the Unit Project

Assigning the Unit Project

The optional unit project consists of two hands-on activities. Either or both parts of the project will give students an opportunity to apply what they have learned about symmetry.

In Part 1: Making Tessellations, students make tessellating shapes by applying symmetry transformations to the sides of a square rhombus and the sides of a nonsquare rhombus. In Part 2: Making a Wreath and a Pinwheel, students explore the symmetries of the various shapes appearing in an origami construction.

Each project can be done by students individually, but students will make more discoveries about tessellations and symmetry if they share ideas about their work in groups or as a whole class.

We recommend that the project be started near the end of the unit, perhaps during Investigation 4.

Part 1: Making Tessellations

In this part of the project, students apply symmetry transformations to attempt to make tessellating shapes from a square and a nonsquare rhombus. The activity is open-ended, and students are given questions to think about as they work. After they have had some exploration time, the class can be brought together to share their discoveries.

The project begins by guiding students as they make a tessellating shape from a square. The exercise will start students thinking about tessellations and about the types of symmetry transformations that can be applied to a square to make a tessellating shape. You may want to check students' work at this stage to make sure they are on the right track.

Materials

- grid paper
- isometric dot paper
- stiff paper
- angle ruler or protractor

Making a Tessellating Shape From a Square

Following the introductory activity, students make their own tessellating shape from a square by performing rotations of pieces cut from a paper square. They can then share their ideas in a class discussion.

One discovery that students might make is that they can cut any shape from one side of a square, rotate it 270° about a vertex, and attach it to the new side to make a figure that tessellates.

In addition, rotating a cutout shape 180° about the midpoint of a side will make a shape that will tessellate. The tessellating figure below was made by cutting a shape from each of three sides of the original square and rotating each cutout 180° about the midpoint of the appropriate side.

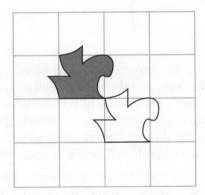

You might explore with the class the relationship between the ways that symmetry transformations can be applied to a square to make a tiling of squares, and the kinds of modifications that can be made to a square to make a new tessellating shape. Take the discussion as far as students are interested.

Making a Tessellating Shape From a Rhombus

Students next make a tessellating shape from a rhombus with angles of 60° and 120°. They will discover that they can cut any shape from one side of a rhombus with these angles, rotate it about a vertex to an adjacent side, and attach it to the new side to make a figure that tessellates.

Challenge the class to try other kinds of modifications. For example, they might try rotating a cutout shape 180° about the midpoint of a side, or rotating a cutout shape that has reflectional symmetry over a perpendicular line through the midpoint of a side. If time permits, they could also try modifying rhombuses that have other interior angles. For rhombuses with other angles, there are restrictions on the cutout shape.

Remind students that if a particular modification results in a tiling that has gaps, the tiling is by definition not a tessellation. For example, the modifications made to the rhombus below result in a shape that does not tessellate.

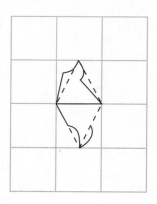

The books *Introduction to Tessellations* and *Teaching Tessellating Art* offer a wealth of ideas about exploring tessellations and symmetry transformations with your class.

Part 2: Making a Wreath and a Pinwheel

Origami is an incredibly rich and complex art form. However, there are some simple but amazing figures that even a beginner can produce successfully. The wreath and pinwheel that students make in this project show again how symmetry plays a fundamental role in much design.

Materials

Eight square pieces of paper of the same size (using four sheets in each of two different colors gives a nice result)

Students will follow the directions in their books to make a wreath from squares of paper and then transform that wreath into a pinwheel. Figures made from origami paper are easier to manipulate, but regular-weight paper will work.

Wreath

Pinwheel

Remind students that the more carefully they cut out the paper squares (which must be the same size), the better their results will be. Also, sharper folds will produce better results. The tricky part of this assembly is tucking one parallelogram into another and folding the tips into the valley. The tips must not "trap" the center part of the parallelogram into which they are being folded.

Answers to the Unit Project

1. **a.** The square has four lines of symmetry (as indicated by the dashed fold lines as shown in Part 2 of the Student Edition) and rotational symmetries of 90°, 180°, and 270°.

   b. The "house" has one line of symmetry, a vertical line through the tip of the "roof," and no rotational symmetry.

   c. The "half-house" has no reflectional symmetry and no rotational symmetry.

   d. The parallelogram has a rotational symmetry of 180° and no reflectional symmetry.

   e. Answers will vary. Possible answer: For a wreath made from two alternating colors, students may say it has rotational symmetries of 90°, 180°, and 270° and no reflectional symmetry. A single-color wreath has rotational symmetries of 45°, 90°, 135°, 180°, 225°, and 270°. The octagonal figure considered as a whole does have eight lines of symmetry, but when the lines separating the individual pieces are taken into consideration, the figure does not have reflectional symmetry. Acknowledge correct reasoning, with the knowledge that some students might choose to ignore the outlines of individual pieces in their search for symmetry.

   f. The pinwheel has no line symmetry. For a pinwheel made from two alternating colors, students may say it has rotational symmetries of 90°, 180°, and 270°. A single-color pinwheel has seven rotational symmetries: 45°, 90°, 135°, 180°, 225°, 270°, and 315°.

2. The two-winged pinwheel has no reflectional symmetry and one rotational symmetry of 180°.

3. Answers will vary. Possible answer: The center can take many shapes, including regular and non-regular quadrilaterals, hexagons, and octagons.

Labsheet 1.1A

Questions A–D

A.

B.

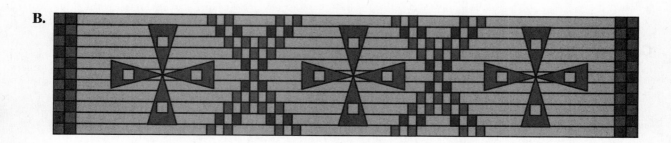

C. **D.**

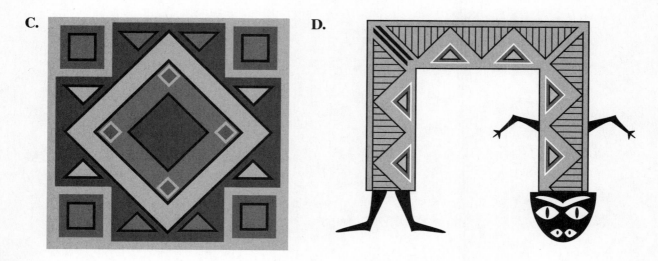

Labsheet 1.1B

Questions E–H

E.

F.

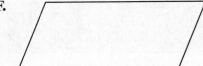

G.

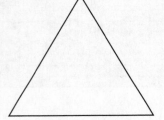

H.

Labsheet 1.2

Pinwheel and Hubcaps

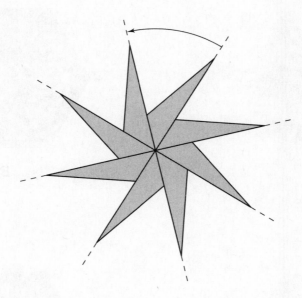

Hubcap 1

Hubcap 2

Labsheet 1.3

Kaleidoscope Designs

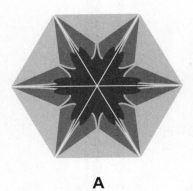

A

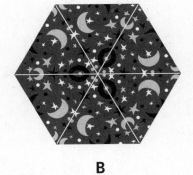

B

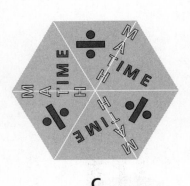

C

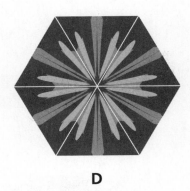

D

E

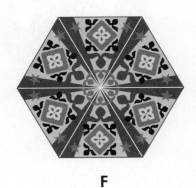

F

Labsheet 1.4

Question B

Labsheet 1ACE Exercises 2-5

2.

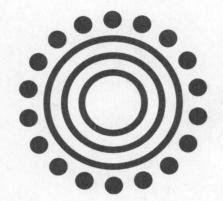

3.

4.

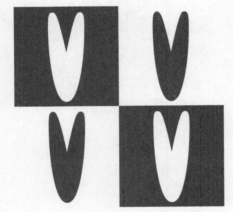

5.

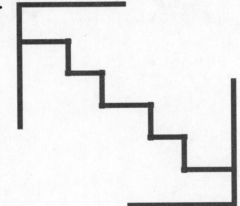

Labsheet 1ACE Exercises 6–9

6.

7.

8.

9.

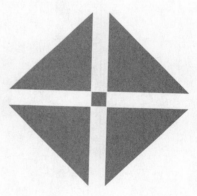

Labsheet 1ACE Exercises 18–19

18.

19.

Labsheet 1ACE Exercises 20-23

....

20.

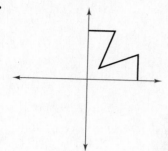

21.

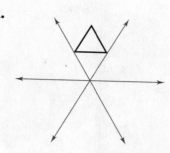

22. ◄ COOKIE ►

23. 1 2 3 4 5 6 7 8 9 0

◄──────────────────►

Labsheet 1ACE Exercises 24–25
....

24.

25.

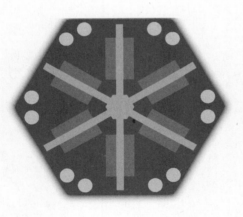

Labsheet 1ACE Exercises 28–29

28.

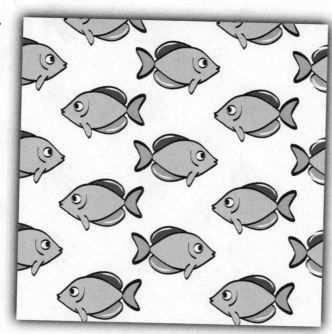

29.

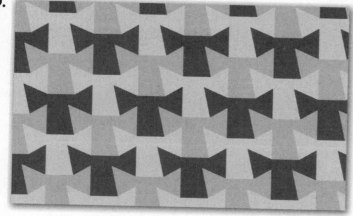

Labsheet 1ACE Exercise 30

30.

Labsheet 1ACE Exercise 46

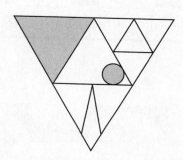

Labsheet 1ACE Exercises 50–53

50.

51.

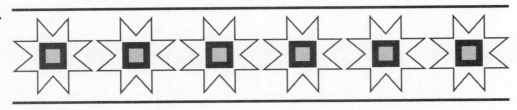

52.

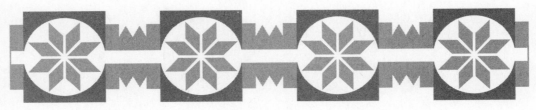

53.

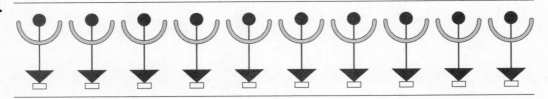

Labsheet 1ACE Exercises 55 and 57

55.

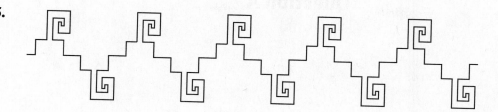

57.

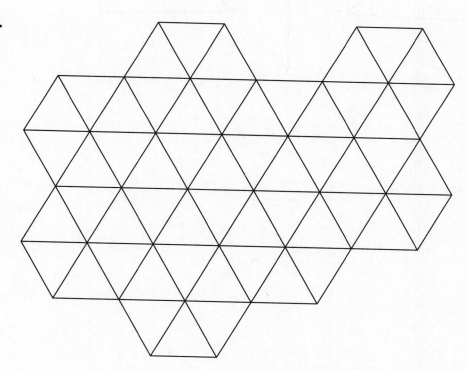

Labsheet 2.1A

Question A

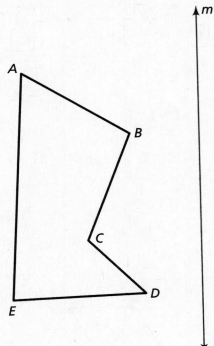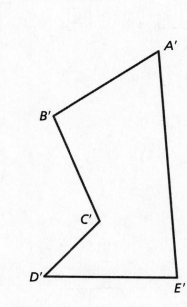

Labsheet 2.1B

Questions B and C

B. 1.

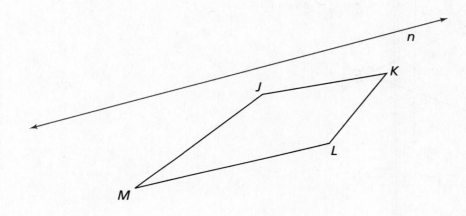

C.

Labsheet 2.1C

Question E

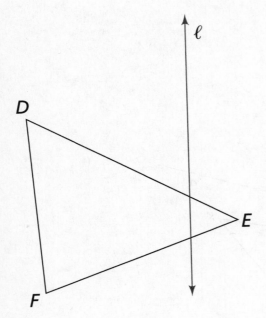

Labsheet 2.2A Compass Star and Flag

A.

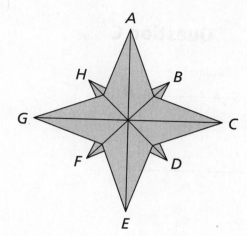

B.

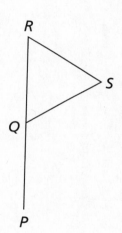

Labsheet 2.2B

Question C

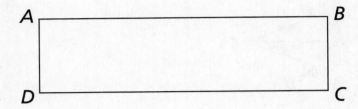

Labsheet 2.3A

Question A

Diagram 1

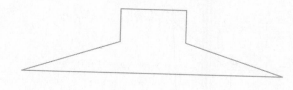

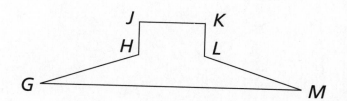

Diagram 2

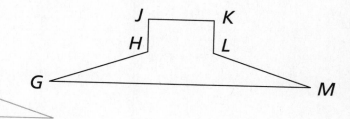

Labsheet 2.3B

Question B

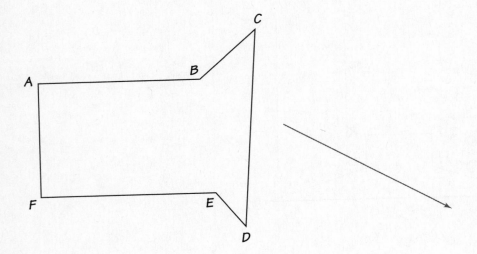

Name _____ Date _____ Class _____

Labsheet 2.4A

Question A

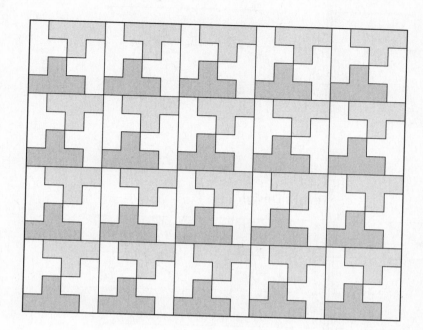

Labsheet 2.4B Question B

Rosslyn's Design

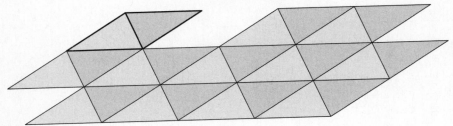

Tevin's Design

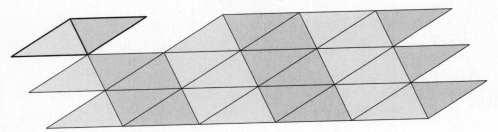

Labsheet 2ACE Exercise 1

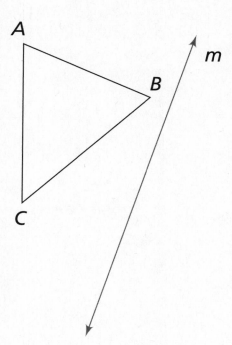

Labsheet 2ACE Exercises 2-3

2.

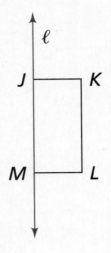

3.

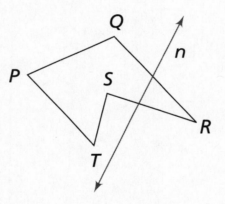

Labsheet 2ACE Exercises 4–5

4.

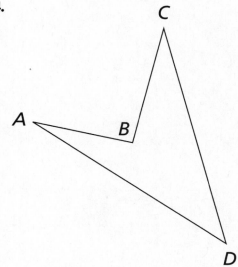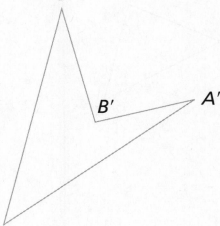

5.

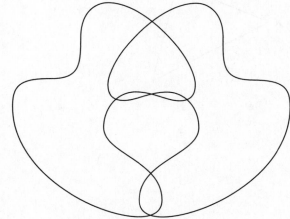

Labsheet 2ACE Exercise 6

a.

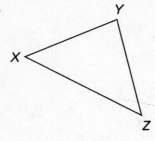

b.

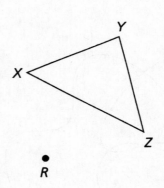

Labsheet 2ACE Exercise 7

a.

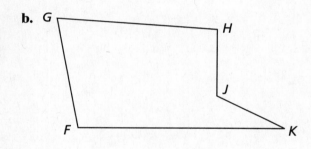

b.

Labsheet 2ACE Exercises 8-9

8.

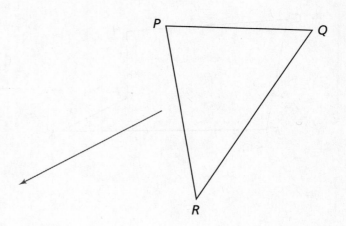

9.

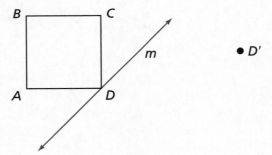

Labsheet 2ACE Exercises 10–13

10.

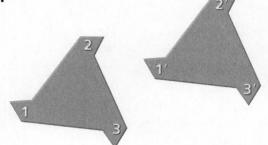

11.

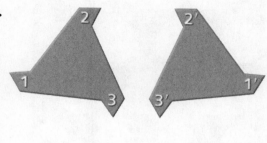

12.

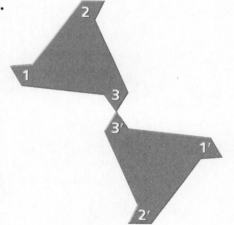

13.

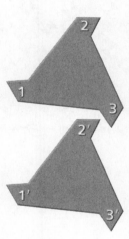

Labsheet 2ACE Exercises 14–15

14.

15.

Labsheet 2ACE Exercise 30

....

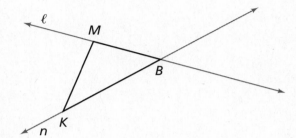

Labsheet 2ACE Exercises 31, 33

31.

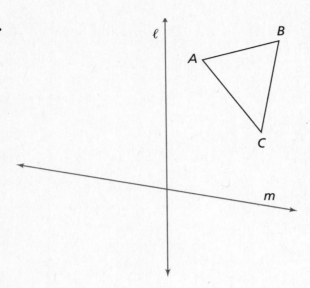

33.

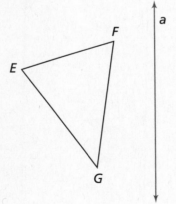

Labsheet 3.1

Questions A–E

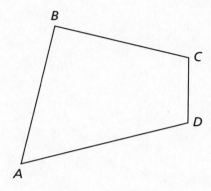
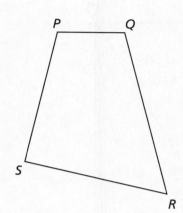

Labsheet 3.2

Questions A–E

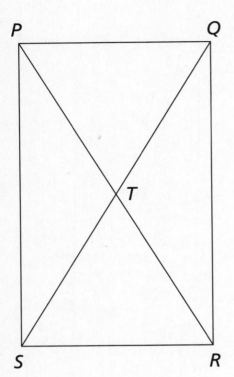

Labsheet 3.3

Matching Game

Figure 1

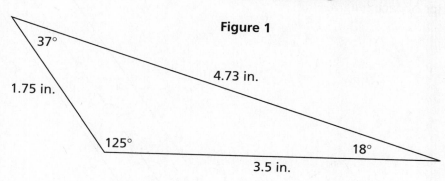

37°

4.73 in.

1.75 in.

125°

18°

3.5 in.

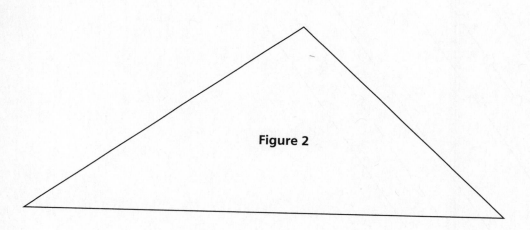

Figure 2

Labsheet 3.4A

Polystrips

A Polystrip set contains six strips of each length.

Labsheet 3.4B Matching Game

D.

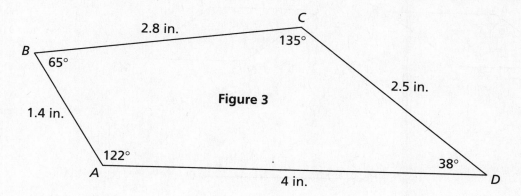

Figure 3

E.

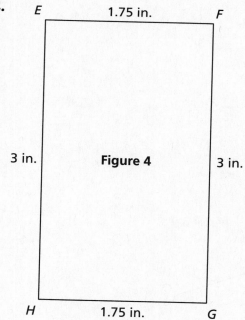

Figure 4

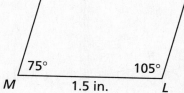

Figure 5

Labsheet 3ACE Exercises 1–4

Kaleidoscopes, Hubcaps, and Mirrors

1.

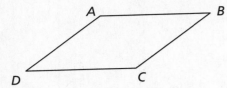
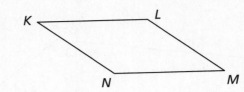

2.

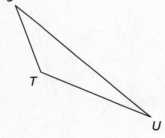
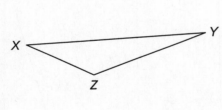

3.

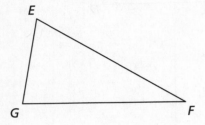
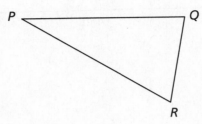

4.

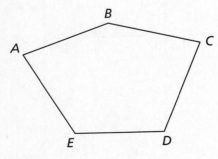
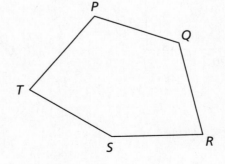

Labsheet 4.1

Engineer's Sketch

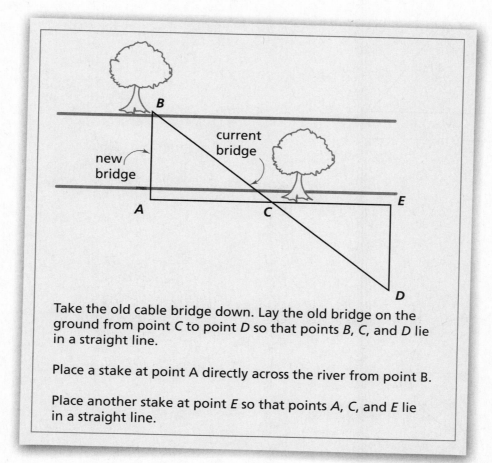

Take the old cable bridge down. Lay the old bridge on the ground from point C to point D so that points B, C, and D lie in a straight line.

Place a stake at point A directly across the river from point B.

Place another stake at point E so that points A, C, and E lie in a straight line.

Questions A and B

A.

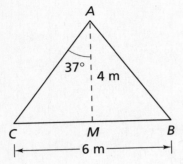

B.

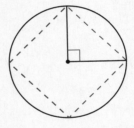

Labsheet 4.2B

Questions C and D

C.

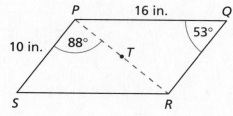

D.

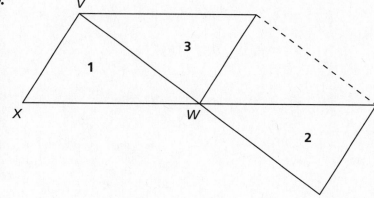

Labsheet 4ACE Exercise 8

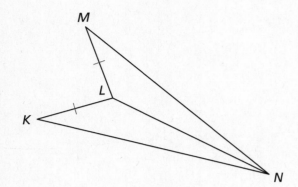

Labsheet 5.1A

Question A

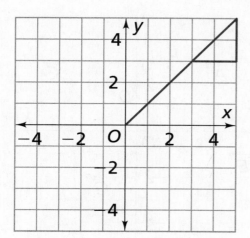

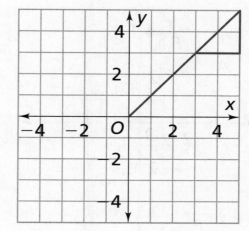

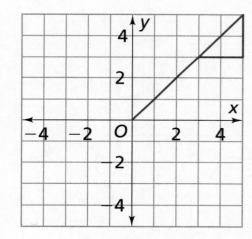

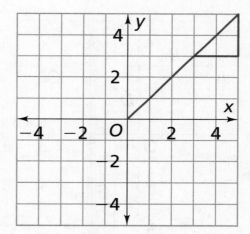

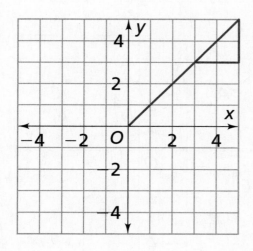

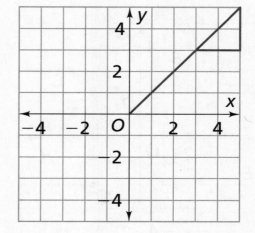

Questions B–E

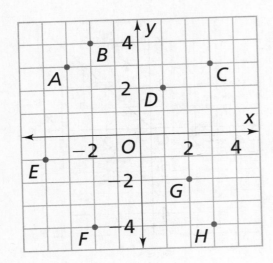

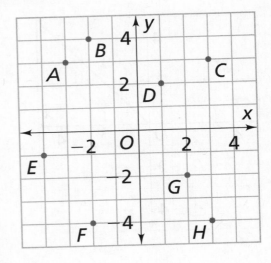

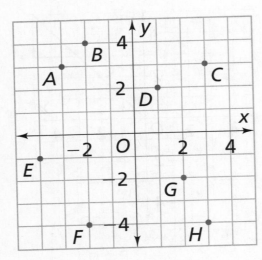

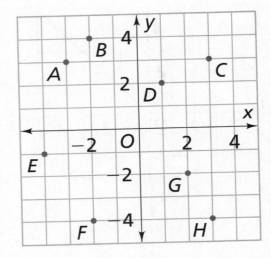

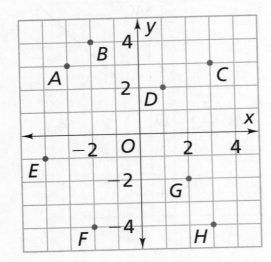

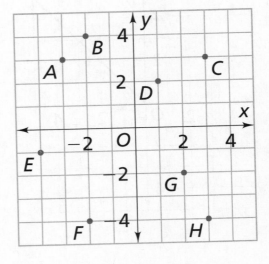

Labsheet 5.2A

Question A

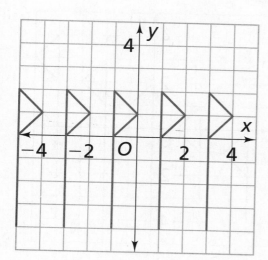

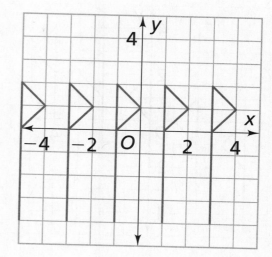

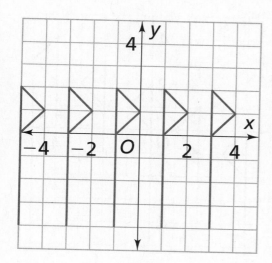

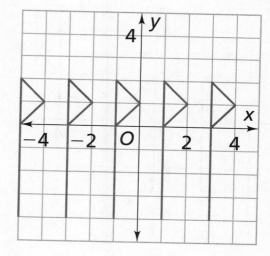

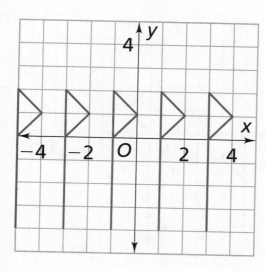

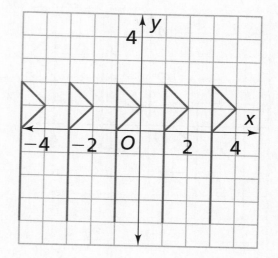

Labsheet 5.2B

Question B

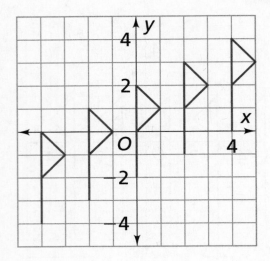

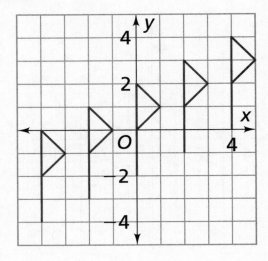

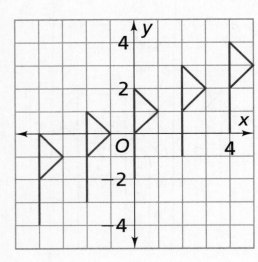

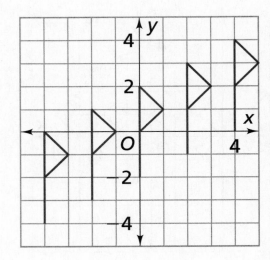

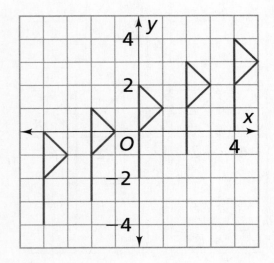

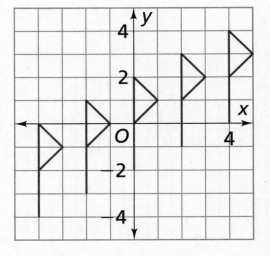

Labsheet 5.2C

Question C

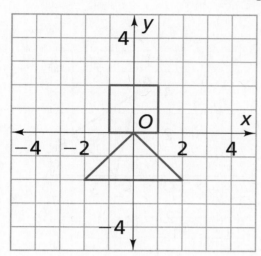
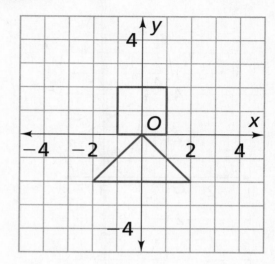
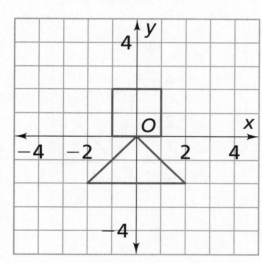
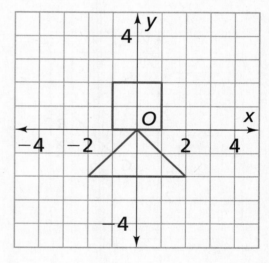
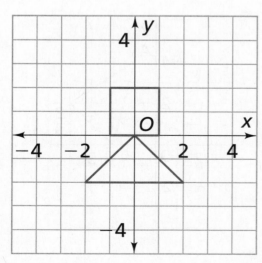
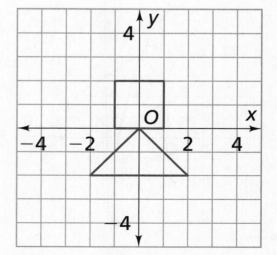

Labsheet 5.3

Question A

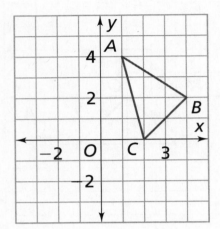

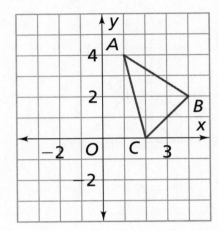

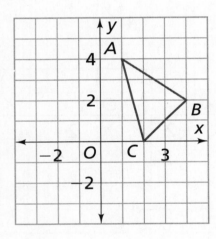

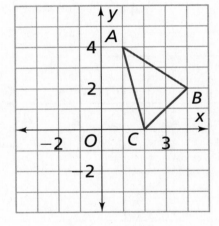

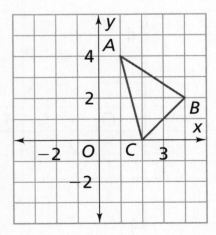

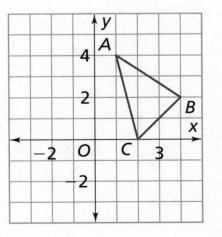

Labsheet 5.4

Questions A and B

A.

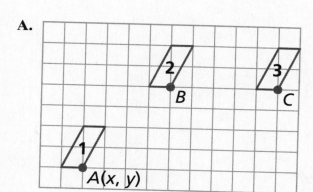

B.

Labsheet 5ACE Exercises 1-3

Kaleidoscopes, Hubcaps, and Mirrors

1.

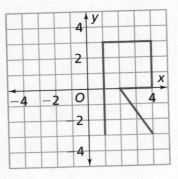

2.

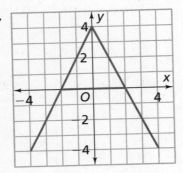

3.

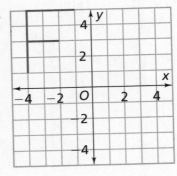

Labsheet 5ACE Exercises 5–14

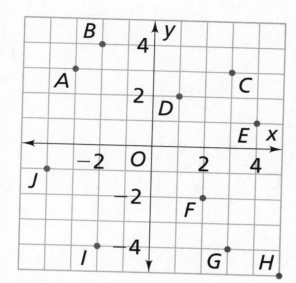

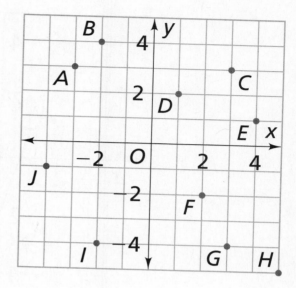

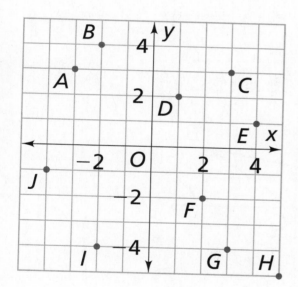

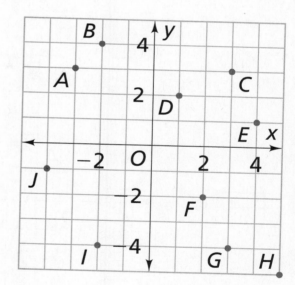

Labsheet 5ACE Exercise 15

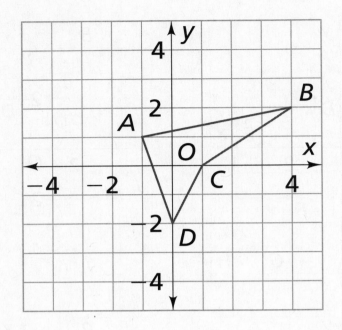

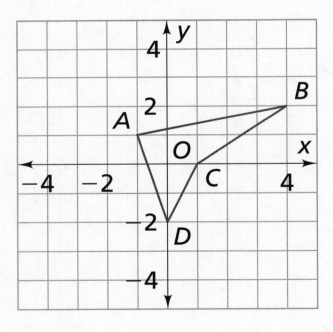

Labsheet 5ACE Exercise 23

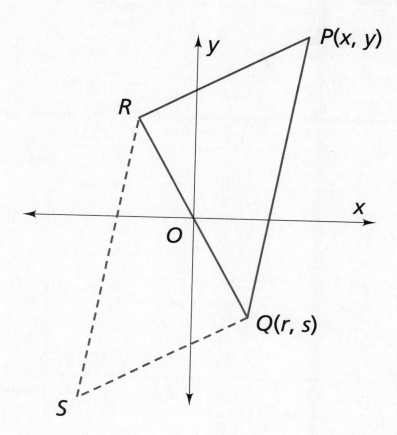

At a Glance

PACING: ________

Mathematical Goals

Launch

Materials

Explore

Materials

Summarize

Materials

B

basic design element A piece of a pattern or design that, when transformed using at least one type of symmetry transformation, will produce the entire design.

C

congruent figures Two figures are congruent if one is an image of the other under a translation, a reflection, a rotation, or some combination of these transformations. Put more simply, two figures are congruent if you can slide, flip, or turn one figure so that it fits exactly on the other. The polygons below are congruent.

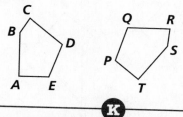

K

kaleidoscope A tube containing colored beads or pieces of glass and carefully placed mirrors. When a kaleidoscope is held to the eye and rotated, the viewer sees colorful, symmetric patterns.

L

line of symmetry A line of symmetry divides a figure into halves that are mirror images. Lines WY and ZX below are lines of symmetry.

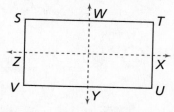

line reflection A transformation that maps each point of a figure to its mirror image, where a line acts as the mirror. Polygon $A'B'C'D'E'$ below is the image of polygon $ABCDE$ under a reflection over the line. If you drew a line segment from a point to its image, the segment would be perpendicular to and bisected by the line of reflection.

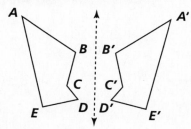

R

reflection symmetry A figure or design has reflection symmetry if you can draw a line that divides the figure into halves that are mirror images. The line that divides the figure into halves is called the *line of symmetry*. The figure below has reflection symmetry about a vertical line through its center. Reflection symmetry is sometimes referred to as *mirror symmetry* or *line symmetry*.

rotation A transformation that turns a figure counterclockwise about a point. Polygon $A'B'C'D'$ below is the image of polygon $ABCD$ under a 60° rotation about point P. If you drew a segment from a point on polygon $ABCD$ to point P and another segment from the point's image to point P, the segments would be the same length and they would form a 60° angle.

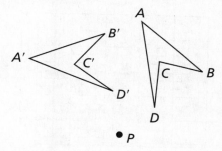

rotation symmetry A figure or design has rotation symmetry if it can be rotated less than a full turn about a point to a position in which it looks the same as the original. The hubcap design below has rotation symmetry with its center as the center of rotation and a 72° angle of rotation. This means that it can be rotated 72°, or any multiple of 72°, about its center point to produce an image that matches exactly with the original.

symmetry An object or design has symmetry if part of it is repeated to produce a balanced pattern. In this unit, you learned about three types of symmetry. The butterfly below has *reflection symmetry*, the fan has *rotation symmetry*, and the wallpaper design has *translation symmetry*.

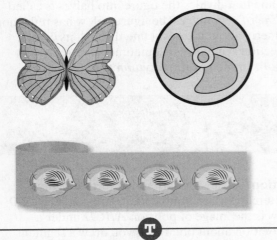

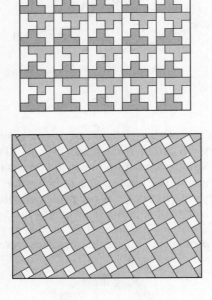

tessellation A design that covers a surface without gaps or overlaps and that consists entirely of copies of a basic design. Tessellations have translation symmetry. The designs below and above right are tessellations.

transformation A geometric operation that relates each point of a figure to an image point. The transformations you studied in this unit—reflections, rotations, and translations—are symmetry transformations. A symmetry transformation produces an image that is identical in size and shape to the original figure.

translation A transformation that slides each point on a figure to an image point a given distance and direction from the original point. Polygon $A'B'C'D'E'$ below is the image of polygon $ABCDE$ under a translation. If you drew line segments from two points to their respective image points, the segments would be parallel and they would have the same length.

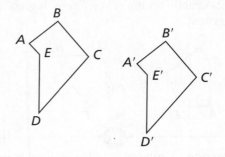

translation symmetry A design has translation symmetry if you can slide it to a position in which it looks exactly the same as it did in its original position. To describe translation symmetry, you need to specify the distance and direction of the translation. Below is part of a design that extends infinitely in all directions. This design has translation symmetry.

Index

Acknowledgments

Team Credits

The people who made up the **Connected Mathematics 2** team—representing editorial, editorial services, design services, and production services—are listed below. Bold type denotes core team members.

Leora Adler, Judith Buice, Kerry Cashman, Patrick Culleton, Sheila DeFazio, Richard Heater, **Barbara Hollingdale, Jayne Holman,** Karen Holtzman, **Etta Jacobs,** Christine Lee, Carolyn Lock, Catherine Maglio, **Dotti Marshall,** Rich McMahon, Eve Melnechuk, Kristin Mingrone, Terri Mitchell, **Marsha Novak,** Irene Rubin, Donna Russo, Robin Samper, Siri Schwartzman, **Nancy Smith,** Emily Soltanoff, **Mark Tricca,** Paula Vergith, Roberta Warshaw, Helen Young

Additional Credits

Diana Bonfilio, Mairead Reddin, Michael Torocsik, nSight, Inc.

Technical Illustration

Schawk, Inc.

Cover Design

tom white.images